METAL CRAFTS IN ARCHITECTURE

GATEWAY TO THE COURT OF ORANGES, SEVILLE
Etching by Louis C. Rosenberg

METAL CRAFTS
IN ARCHITECTURE

BRONZE · BRASS · CAST IRON · COPPER
LEAD · LIGHTING FIXTURES · TIN
· SPECIFICATIONS ·

GERALD K. GEERLINGS

NEW YORK
CHARLES SCRIBNER'S SONS

CONTENTS

RAISON D'ÊTRE

IT is presumptuous to assume that any one volume could treat exhaustively of all the decorative metals (except wrought iron) which are used in architecture. From the outset it is hoped that the reader realizes that this book makes no claim to have mapped all the ramifications of historical and craftsmanship "research," but has only charted a number of routes which the interested layman, architect, and craftsman can pursue more leisurely if they find the scenery to their liking. It is a road map of arterial highways with the main milestones and signposts marked, rather than a detailed contour map with every footpath plotted.

From a survey of the existing books on the decorative metals used in architecture it becomes at once apparent that they have been compiled and written from various view-points, usually of a general historical nature, but never from a purely architectural aspect. In no single one is there a parallel presentation of the salient characteristics of the metals which embellish a building, a description of the manner in which these materials are worked so that the designer may come to an appreciation of the inherent potentialities as well as the limitations, nor a concise historical background of the various metals in various countries, amplified by architectural illustrations.

In this unfortunate day of *presto tempo* we do not luxuriously possess either time or means to retire to a cloister garth and pore over a hundred tomes on the history of each metal, or to wander from town to town, and, with amiability encouraged by pipe and cups, engage in pleasant conversation with the metal craftsmen. On the contrary, in the average architect's office, when the sketches for a building are in a tentative and rushed state, their ultimate execution is always doubtful, so that for the metal work it becomes a practice of hastily "indicating something" on which preliminary estimates are obtained. If the building comes to be built it is felt necessary to follow fairly closely on the heels of what has been previously shown, with the result that too often the erected metal work bears the stigma of being embryonic in design, haphazard in execution, and wanting in good taste. It is hoped that this book may be of intrinsic value to the architect who has not the time for extensive research and who yet is intent on so designing metal work that from the very first sketch it will serve a purpose, look its part, and be suitable to the metal from which it is made. The contents of the book are so arranged that if the reader be interested in a certain metal he can, at the beginning of the chapter, turn to a concise historical background; if a problem in design confronts him he can turn to the next part which describes how his *opus* will be executed, stating what limitations of the metal he should observe and what natural qualities he should enhance, and finally in each chapter there is a group of illustrations which give a representative idea of what has been accomplished in the past. The last chapter is solely for the architect wishing information on specifying the various metals in decorative usage; its purpose is to provide a skeleton form for general conditions which will exclude unfair competition and encourage a higher type of craftsmanship.

It will be indulgently forgiven, the author hopes, if certain historical facts or outstanding monuments have been unintentionally overlooked; fifty pages of text which attempt to portray a bird's-eye vista of territory which covers thousands, are bound to be guilty of nearsightedness here and far-sightedness there. The author read practically all the available material in the English language (and struggled with a little French and German) at the main library of New York City, as well as the documents in several private libraries. However, it is obviously impossible to select with infallibility all material which would universally be accepted as of the foremost importance, particularly in view of the great condensation here necessary. Then too, the ever-present difficulty was to allot space in proportion to the architectural importance of a metal in relation to modern application.

In the subject-matter concerning craftsmanship the author felt himself on surer ground. The information about each metal was acquired by interviewing the first-class craftsmen within reasonable distance in and around New York City, and observing the progress of the metal from rough through finished state. Just as no two artists would paint the same landscape with the same pigments or apply these alike, so no two interrogated craftsmen worked the same metal in exactly the same manner in all respects. The material in the book is not meant to split hairs over the means of working metals in all their technical intricacies; the descriptions of essentials are intended to give the designer and layman a correct idea of how results in metal are obtained. Craftsmen who generously co-operated by giving the author first-hand information and explained the various steps in the foundries and shops, have also kindly read over the manuscript. The author is therefore indebted to them not only for information and assistance, but for helping to shoulder the responsibility for the authenticity of the facts.

One hundred and fifty pages of illustrations will be as guilty of omitting some of the thousands of *chefs d'œuvre* as the text may sometimes be lacking in important names, dates, and facts. Some illustrations which were desired could not be procured. Others were excluded because of work ably designed but badly executed, and vice versa. Some examples which should be allotted their place of honor, the author may not even have known of, in which case he tenders his humblest apologies to craftsmen past and present.

In the pleasant meanderings of the author through the foundries and shops of the various craftsmen, he became increasingly impressed with the fact that unless the artisan takes personal pride in his work he is in the wrong field. Unless there is a definite gain accruing from the joy of creating, then the metal game must be a severely disappointing one; if any one is intent on mere financial profits it must be galling indeed to try to make them in decorative metal work. How bitter to know the cost of each hammer blow or the expense of each moment spent in perfecting a mould! No different of course and no less productive of art, is the architect whose organization moves on a cost-sheet basis, and whose completed plans and details are not determined by arriving at a thoughtful and successful effect, but by a schedule of drafting costs which prearranges the date when certain work must be finished for blue-printing, regardless of æsthetic results. Both such persons, while pathetic in having the wrong jobs, are nevertheless culpable for much of the eye misery foisted on the helpless public. Some philanthropist should endow all "business-getters" in the architectural and metal craft fields who have not the artistic welfare of a job at heart, with stock-market tickers plus plenty of tape and capital.

The genuine architect and the genuine craftsman never lead affluent lives, but they can have genuinely successful ones. The jobs they execute may be small, but the return can be inversely great. Who can live through the development of a building or a bronze ingot from its sullen embryonic stage to its final completion, without experiencing all the emotions of the combined crucial moments of a general, a judge, an adventurer, a poet, and a mother? The sheer exultation of an idea conceived, the lurking doubt of its not being executed, the throbbing energy of a thing in the making, the rich pain of unavailing endeavor, the fear of failure, the intoxication of achievement—these are the daily tonic of the artist dealing in architecture and in metal. And so, for such unstinted compensation, what wonder is it that their path should not be strewn with paltry dollars?

The genuine architect is coming to realize that the genuine metal craftsman is a vital part of his organization, since he himself has too many other responsibilities to be able to fill the rôle of metal designer and craftsman. He is learning that he must know how to think and draw in terms of metal, but that the actual effect, for good or bad, is dependent upon the imagination and personality of his confrère, the craftsman. The information on the craftsmanship of each metal is meant to give the architect some insight into the manner in which the work is carried on, so that he will have a sounder conception of how to design. But more than that, it is hoped to stimulate sufficient interest in the metal crafts so that the architect will see and enjoy the pageantry of metal in the making, for only by so doing can he come to a riper understanding of what may be expected and what can be achieved.

When in the employ of York & Sawyer some years ago the author became acquainted with Mr. Samuel Yellin, Philadelphia, through his work on the Federal Reserve Bank of New York City. Before our going abroad for a year in 1924–25, Mr. Yellin made a number of valuable suggestions for collecting the material for a book on wrought iron work. That was the beginning of an effort which only now is beginning to crystallize in book form. The first idea of treating only wrought iron has expanded into this book's embracing bronze, brass, cast iron, copper, lead, etc., while wrought iron will comprise a separate volume of about the same size to be issued shortly.

The underlying idea of this book seemed

gradually to shape itself into pointing out that metal work to be beautiful (in the Greek sense) must serve a useful purpose, and be so designed as best to display the natural endowments of the material. Just before going to press the author was given a reprint of a lecture called "Right Making," by B. J. Fletcher, Director of the Municipal Art Schools, Birmingham, England, delivered at the London School of Economics, Aldwych, January 14, 1925. With pleasurable surprise we found that it was as though it had formed an unconscious outline for the book while in the making. Three excerpts are therefore quoted because they sound the keynote of good craftsmanship.

As regards *fitness of purpose*, the first tenet necessary to genuine craftsmanship, the lecture states: "It is a mistake to think that art is hampered by structural or utilitarian requirements; on the contrary: it is from these that it receives its reason and inspiration. The beauty of the perfect forms of natural things comes of necessity. From consideration of the simple shapes of leaves or seeds, to the complex and beautiful shapes and modeling of bones, we must conclude that the inevitable rightness of design is due to the insistent claims of use and purpose; each line or twist is there to fulfill some definite work and duty. . . . On the other hand, it is salutary to remember that where artists and craftsmen have had entire freedom of conditions, some of their worst work has been done. . . .

"As outstanding mistakes, imitation of one material by another will be remembered: paper made to look like cambric, tiles or terra-cotta made to look like stone or marble, iron made to look like bronze, cotton to look like silk. The stupidity of these needs no comment; art is never artifice. With such we shall make no mistake. It is with the just-possible technique, the nearly good or the clever handling which is not quite sympathetic with its medium that we go wrong, and in the whole range of fine craftsmanship it is this adjustment of treatment to material which is most often in error. As a skilful violinist makes the utmost of the characteristic quality of his instrument, so will the good craftsman deal with his material. . . .

"Some good and beautiful materials have their individual character degraded in a foolish attempt to make them imitate things which are more expensive. These, and all other shams, are dead against appreciation of beauty or art. By working *with* a material, not against it, we may get beauty.

"This matter may possibly be made clearer by taking a parallel from a totally different source. We would have dogs of pure breed and not mongrels; a strain of spaniel discredits a greyhound. We should know and appreciate the characteristic qualities of brass or wood and feel when the treatment is alien to the material as certainly as we pick out an alien strain in a fox terrier. But in articles of brass and wood we are so used to the presence of treatments proper to stone or marble that we do not see that the treatment is alien and the result a mongrel. It is possibly true to say that of the miles of cast-iron railings which have been made during the past century none has repeated the good cast-metal tradition which died about 1840, or made beauty in any other manner from emphasis of the qualities and nature of cast iron. Most of it imitates wrought iron. It is interesting to notice in this connection that errors of treatment are most frequent and greatest in those materials which are most easily modeled or moulded. There is, for instance, in modern times, little terra-cotta or plaster work which shows the characteristic qualities of these two materials. On the other hand, in refractory materials, like wrought iron, or hard stone, the suitability of the treatment for its material is more often seen. Materials difficult to work keep the craftsman in hand, make him search for essentials, get most profit from his labour, and force him to work with, and not against, his material."

IN ACKNOWLEDGMENT

EXCEPT for the whole-hearted co-operation which the author found at every hand, it would not have been possible to include the material in each chapter on the craftsmanship of the various metals. We are indebted not only to the various craftsmen for the information they contributed, the suggestions they made, and the insight into the metal crafts which their shops and foundries afforded, but also for one of the most instructive and thoroughly enjoyable experiences of a lifetime. The pent-up excitement contained within the four walls of a foundry is scarcely equalled anywhere else during peacetime, while the pageantry is so theatrical that to this interested onlooker it constantly gave the impression of seeing the best-show-on-earth on a free pass. For that "pass" and for the resultant enjoyable experience the author does not know how to make proper acknowledgment.

This book, as explained in the *Raison d'Être*, is the outgrowth of what started to be one work including all the decorative metals used in building, but the material in this volume was divorced from wrought iron, which is to be a companion to it. For the original idea of compiling a book the author is indebted to Mr. Samuel Yellin, and while the metals treated in this one are not his favorite medium, wrought iron, to him the author wishes to express his deep gratitude for the stimulating influence he has been.

The metal concerning which the greatest number of pages in this book deal, is bronze, and the person to whom the author is deepest in debt, is Mr. Alexander H. Burgess, president of Jno. Williams, Inc. When two articles appeared in *Pencil Points* (June and July, 1927) by the author under the title, "The Architect, the Artisan—and Bronze," the technical information and the illustrations were obtained from Mr. Burgess. The same material has been reworked and amplified here, and since it was done with his aid, this acknowledgment should also be amplified. We made ourselves a thorn-in-the-flesh to Mr. Burgess for over a year, borrowed documents from his library for that length of time, and telephoned him and nagged him for advice when he was uncomfortably busy. Yet withal he has remained good-natured and friendly. In the chapter on "Bronze Crafts-

manship" the technical information has come largely from him, and William Donald Mitchell, vice-president of Jno. Williams, Inc., as have the specifications on page 193, not to forget the photographs taken in his foundry (Figures 18 to 23 inclusive, 25 and 26).

The companion book to this, "Wrought Iron in Architecture," has been greatly aided in its compilation by the enthusiastic efforts of Mr. Carl Weiler, of the J. G. Braun Company, and while the material in this volume does not treat specifically of the subject in which he is most interested (wrought iron), yet we are greatly indebted to him for the use of his library and the energy he has expended in helping us to secure illustrations and information.

The Victoria and Albert Museum, London, the Metropolitan Museum of Art, New York City, and the Pennsylvania Museum, Philadelphia, have generously assisted to the greatest possible extent in the matter of providing illustrations.

To pursue the order of the various chapters in the book, and to take them in turn with our creditors listed for each, the author wishes to express his gratitude and appreciation to the various individuals who have so freely given of their time and the benefit of their experience:

Bronze:—To Mr. Burgess (as noted above); to the Gorham Company, for valuable suggestions pertaining both to craftsmanship and specifications; to the Superb Bronze & Iron Company, for many valuable suggestions on modern foundry and estimating problems, on the *cire perdue* process, and for the pleasure of seeing a model foundry and shop; to the Wm. H. Jackson Company, for being shown all branches and ramifications of its plant; and to the American Pin Company at Ansonia, Conn., for being shown the extruded bronze process and being given the important information concerned therewith.

Cast Iron:—To Mr. Frank C. Royer, of the Smyser-Royer Company, for his comradeship and sympathetic help, for his pains in showing us the various processes at his company's plant, and for his assistance in the preparation of the material on craftsmanship and specifications, and for the views taken in the foundry (Figures 132 to 136 inclusive); to Mr. Lawrence McKinney, of James McKinney & Son, for his

5

thorough knowledge and research which led to a greatly improved manuscript, for suggestions and criticisms as to specifications, and for a number of sketches which served as a basis for Figure 129; to my good friend, Richard Koch, for the information relative to the old cast iron in his beloved New Orleans, and for the photographs of that city (unfortunately cramped quarters prevented reproducing some which we should have liked to include); and to Mr. A. S. Richey, of Richey, Browne & Donald, and Mr. Ossa Sowers, metallurgist and chemist, for their valuable suggestions and criticism of the manuscript.

Copper:—To the Copper & Brass Research Association for its whole-hearted co-operation in every possible way in supplying us with the information it has collected on the subject, and suggesting sources for further information and illustrations; to Mr. Theodore E. Hergert for conducting us through all departments of his shop, explaining each operation in detail, and for his suggestions concerning the craftsmanship of stamped copper; to Klein & Kavanagh for their suggestions as to the technique of *repoussé* work, and specifications.

Lead:—To Henry Hope & Sons for showing us the manner in which lead is cast according to mediæval traditions, for explaining the various steps in the process, and for their genuine desire to be of the greatest possible service; to Klein & Kavanagh for their suggestions in both craftsmanship and specifications for *repoussé* lead work; and to Mr. Charles G. Kemp, of Richmond & Kemp, for the interesting observations he has made concerning the combinations of lead ornament with wrought iron designs which were commonly thought of as being entirely of iron.

Current Developments:—To the Birmingham Guild for its constant assistance and valued suggestions, for the inspiration of its enamelled work in which the beauty of the material is equalled by the sensitiveness and imagination of the design, and for the aid in compiling the specifications; to the Frink Company for its assistance in obtaining the information on depositing copper on glass; and to the International Nickel Company for the information on monel metal.

Specifications:—To Alexander H. Burgess, the Gorham Company, and Lawrence McKinney, as noted above for bronze and cast iron: to Mr. W. W. Beach, through the courtesy of *Pencil Points*, in looking over the entire manuscript on specifications, and for making valued criticisms and suggestions; to the Allied Building Metal Industries of New York City, for pamphlets and suggestions; and to York & Sawyer for the privilege of quoting their bronze specifications of the Royal Bank of Canada, Montreal.

"Specifications" is the last chapter, but there are still two large outstanding accounts which are related to all chapters. The first is in the name of my wife, who spent endless hours at the New York Library hunting down facts, verifying dates and spelling, and who helped with the manuscript from the first rough drafts to the completed galley-proof. What is more praiseworthy still has been her constant enthusiasm, in place of which she would have been more than justified in objecting to the empty family coffer during these many months of concentrated work on the book, and the expenditure of most evenings, Sundays, holidays and such similar occasions when a husband ordinarily is not a metallic recluse.

And the second debt is to the publishers. The end of the long trail has been the most pleasant of the entire route, not because the end of the adventure was in sight, but because of the congenial relationship which they have created. As the last page-proof is read and the last caption appended to the last half-tone, it will not be the occasion for rejoicing which in the early days of the book the author had imagined it, but rather sincere regret that the curtain has been rung down, the backstage cleared, and the properties folded away.

December 1, 1928.   G. K. G.

BRONZE: HISTORY

WHILE bronze most probably originated in the Caucasus, its architectural application was not of real importance until the heyday of Rome. Between the time of the discovery of the copper-tin alloy, and its use in buildings centuries later, ensues a long and fascinating development which is naturally of greater interest to the archæologist than to the professional or layman interested in Occidental architecture. In the following pages the consideration will therefore be confined chiefly to the usage of bronze in European edifices. While the bronzes of south and east Asia not only antedate anything of importance of Western civilization, but in addition are perhaps of more delicate detail and jewelry-like execution, and while their study would go far toward better appreciation of what the metal can accomplish, yet for want of space we can do no more here than express the hope that those vitally interested in bronze will investigate specimens in museums and books. It is of interest that the Chinese and Japanese seem always to have known of what certain American foundrymen regard as a trade secret—the *cire perdue* process (page 23).

From the Caucasus two main streams of influence spread to Europe: one pursued the meanderings of the Danube through the Balkans, continued down the Rhine through Germany to the Baltic, and terminated in the Scandinavian peninsula; the other traversed Asia Minor into Egypt, crossed the Mediterranean into Greece, and followed the coast to Italy, France, and Spain. While both are of importance, the latter has exerted the greater effect upon the architecture of this country, and, therefore, will be chiefly considered in subdivisions of Italy, France, Spain, and England; Germany is the chief protagonist of the former.

The histories of brass and bronze are so closely allied because of their metallic content that, except for the so-called "monumental brasses" (considered in the chapter on "Brass," pages 95–96), the two will be treated simultaneously here. Egyptian bronze almost uniformly consisted of 88 parts of copper to 12 of tin; Greek coins of Hiero and Alexander, as well as the statues of the Periclean period, were pure bronze of copper and tin; but in certain early Roman works some lead was present, and, in the time of Augustus and after, zinc was often added. Romanesque and Renaissance formulæ varied greatly, sometimes minimizing the tin and increasing the zinc content to such an extent that the alloy virtually became brass which lent itself to *repoussé* work.

In several respects the histories of bronze and wrought iron differ radically. In the case of the latter the expense of the metal was seldom a hindrance to its being employed; it has been used almost continuously since the twelfth century in all countries; and the greatest achievements were wrought by the craftsmen themselves. Bronze, on the other hand, was always limited in usage because of the relative rarity and expense of the component metals; it was used only intermittently after the fall of Rome; and the best works were created by a collaboration of sculptor or designer with the founder, for only rarely was the latter a creative artist. Where in iron the tendency was to overdo the texture and design *motifs*, in bronze the full range of delicate modeling and surfacing was sensed but rarely and then only in the best work. Although bronze is an "eternal metal" compared to iron, its intrinsic value for cannon, and for replenishing depleted coffers, so consistently made inroads on the artistic expressions of previous periods that a lesser percentage of architectural bronze is extant than iron. It is obviously unwise to make the comparison in this way, since there was less bronze than iron used, but the astounding facts that only one equestrian statue (of Marcus Aurelius) from Roman days, and only sixty-four sets of doors up to and including the fifteenth century, still remain, make one feel it has been treated less respectfully by politics and time than has iron. Because of their variance in resisting corrosion the reverse would be expected.

From the time of the supremacy of the Nile to that of the Tiber, the process of mastering bronze technique was a gradual and a consistent one. The alloy was used in Egypt from the time of the sixth dynasty and attained enviable perfection in casting; the qualities of the metal were appreciated and expressed both in the modeling and the sense of design, offering a good foundation for the Grecian triumphs which followed. In the early seventh century B. C., Glaucos of Chios discovered a means of soldering bronze, which permitted far greater elasticity in the possibilities of design. The zenith of Greek bronzes was probably reached from about 460 to 430 B. C. (Phidias 500?–432? B. C.). Casting technique was consummated and damascening was introduced from the East. The Etrurians were not the equal of the Greeks in statuary, yet for furniture, armor, votive statuettes, lamps, vessels, etc., their castings were nevertheless admirable. Enriched by centuries of the craft experience of their vanquished predecessors, the Romans carried on the accepted traditions, producing not only hosts of statues but the first Occidental doors as well. Those of the Pantheon in Rome are said to be the only ones *in situ*. Unfortunately, only a few of the many Rome once could boast have survived, transplanted in churches, so that the history of architectural bronze is sadly incomplete from the very beginning.

In the history of architectural bronze one would expect to find the metal used as diversely as was wrought iron. Yet in turning through all the documents available one is impressed, if not depressed, by the emphasis being placed almost entirely upon sculptural objects, lighting fixtures, occasional pieces of furniture, and properties of religious ceremonies or organizations. It is astonishing that scarcely ever was

FIG. 2.—DETAIL OF BRONZE DOORS OF PRINCIPAL FAÇADE, ST. JOHN LATERAN, ROME

bronze used in grilles and railings, the forms in which wrought iron is employed more than any other. Doors comprise the most important usage and are the best indicators of the various centres and periods at which the craft flourished. First were the Roman doors, and then a cessation until the sixth century, when Justinian ordered the doors for St. Sophia. Another lapse ensued until the ninth century, when the first Frankish doors were cast for Aix-la-Chapelle and Peterhausen, to be followed by a few others in Germany during the eleventh century. Coincident with these latter were a number cast by Greeks at Constantinople. The beginning of Italian activity in the twelfth century culminated three centuries later in the modeling and casting perfection of the Ghiberti doors of the Florence Baptistry (pages 52–57).

According to the best authorities there are but sixty-four sets of bronze doors in existence still remaining from the earliest architectural history up to and including the end of the fifteenth century. The list which follows is taken from J. Travenor Perry's book, "Dinanderie," supplemented by dates and facts from a number of scattered sources. Because doors executed after the sixteenth century have derived their inspiration from those preceding, and none have exceeded the pre-sixteenth century ones in beauty or inventiveness of *parti*, the last pair here given are those of Westminster Abbey.

FIG. 1.—MAIN EXTERIOR DOORS, PANTHEON, ROME

DATE	ORIGIN	LOCATION, AND AUTHOR (IF KNOWN)	PAGE†
?	Roman	Rome, Pantheon, *in situ*, erected by Emperor Hadrian at restoration about 124 A. D.	8
?	"	Rome, Temple of Romulus	
?	"	Rome, Baths of Caracalla, now in St. John Lateran, Baptistry	
?	"	Curia, now on main façade of St. John Lateran, Rome	8
c. 560	Greek	Constantinople, St. Sophia, end of narthex	
"	"	Constantinople, St. Sophia, atrium (16 doors)	
" (?)	"	Venice, St. Mark, Baptistry	
"	"	Venice, St. Mark, north door of north transept	
c. 800	Frankish	Aix-la-Chapelle, Minster, west front	
?	"	Peterhausen, Constanz	
c. 1000	German	Mainz, Cathedral, ordered by Archbishop Willigis in 998	
1015	"	Hildesheim, Cathedral (from St. Michael's)	16
11th C.	"	Gnesen, Cathedral	16
"	"	Novgorod, Russia; St. Sophia	
"	Greek	Suzdal, Volhynia, Russia	
"	"	Moscow, Russia	
1066	"	Monte Cassino, Italy; inlaid with silver; only parts remaining; cast by Staurachios	
1066	"	Amalfi, Cathedral	
1061–72 (?)	"	Rome, San Paolo Fuori le Mura; destroyed in fire of 1824; only	
1066–71 (?)	"	parts remaining; had peculiar damascening or inlaying with silver wire; cast by Staurachios	
1070 or 1080 (?)	German	Augsburg, Cathedral	17
1076	Greek	Monte Santangelo, Italy; cast by Staurachios	34
1087	"	Atrani, San Salvadore; have raised cross characteristic of doors of St. Sophia; cast by Staurachios	
1099	" (?)	Salerno, Cathedral	
?	"	Venice, St. Mark, front right-hand door*	
?	?	Venice, St. Mark, front left-hand door*	
1112	Italian	Venice, St. Mark, central door	
1115	"	Canosa di Puglia, Tomb of Boemund; probably altered (?); cast by Ruggero of Melfi	36
1119	"	Troja, Cathedral, west door; by Oderisius of Benevento	
1127	"	Troja, Cathedral, south door; both west and this door of Cathedral have portraits of inlaid silver lines, of bishops and others including artist; by Oderisius of Benevento	} 38, 39
1150	"	Benevento, Cathedral; door of 12 compartments, more Roman than Byzantine; by Oderisius of Benevento (?)	40, 41
1171	"	Verona, San Zeno; 48 panels beaten and not cast, bolted and nailed to wood doors; *relievos* of Biblical subjects	37
1175	"	Trani, Cathedral; by Barisanus of Trani	
1179	"	Ravello, Cathedral; 54 panels bolted to backing, joints covered by broad bands of ornament of interlacing circles also framed in panels; by Barisanus of Trani	42, 43
1180 (?)	"	Monreale, Cathedral, north door; by Barisanus of Trani	44
1180	"	Pisa, Cathedral; by Bonanno da Pisa; smaller ones in transept remain, larger ones lost in fire replaced by those of Giovanni da Bologna	} 46, 47, 49
1186	"	Monreale, Cathedral, west door; by Bonanno da Pisa	45
1191	"	St. Clemente di Causauria, near Pescara in the Abruzzi; plates nailed to wood core; subjects in relief	
1203 (?)	"	Rome, St. John Lateran, Sacristry; by Albertus and Petrus "Lausenensis" (?)	
c. 1300	"	Venice, St. Mark, outside gates; by Bertuccius	
c. 1330	"	Florence, Baptistry, south door; by Andrea Pisano; originally at Baptistry, San Giovanni; now surmounted by rich frieze modeled and partly worked by Lorenzo Ghiberti	50
1337	Spanish	Toledo, Cathedral	
"	"	Cordova	
?	"	Seville, Puerta del Perdon	
14th C.	Russian	Alexandrova Slaboda	
1403–24	Italian	Florence, Baptistry, east door; Ghiberti	} 52–57
1425–52	"	Florence, Baptistry, north door; Ghiberti	} inc.
1439 (?), 1445 (?)	"	Rome, St. Peter's, main door; Filarete assisted by Simone	58, 59
1505 (?)	English	London, Westminster Abbey, Henry VII's Chapel; brass gates Gothic in design and construction	

*Said to have been intended for St. Sophia. †Page number of illustrations listed where possible in this column.

To continue with a summary of architectural employments of bronze: except for doors, almost every other form is confined to church appurtenances. Railings or grilles are rare; the earliest protective one is of pierced sheet bronze at the Church of the Nativity at Bethlehem, possibly of the fifth or sixth century. A similar one may have existed about the seventh century in the crypt of the Church of Sant' Apollinare in Classe Fuori, just outside of Ravenna. Some still exist at Aix-la-Chapelle; perhaps the most beautiful of all is at Prato (pages 64–65). Paxes, hand-warmers (*pomme de cuivre*), and mortars were frequently richly ornamented, as were pyxes, ciboria and monstrances. Because of frequent raids during the Middle Ages, the sacred remains of saints were placed in portable coffers which were sometimes ornamented with bronze. Crosses and censers, while not strictly architectural forms, showed the current tendencies in modeling, but these are of such wide variation as to defy summing up into definite classifications. Candelabra, used in church ceremonies, offered opportunities in both form and modeling, and are represented by such famous ones as in Durham Cathedral; Milan Cathedral (with its seven branches, page 170); Chapel of St. Anne, Prague Cathedral; Essen, Germany (998); Magdeburg (? thirteenth century), and one of the finest of brass, 16 feet high, at St. Leonard, Léau. Crosiers were beautifully and richly designed. Lecterns were a common form—one of the earliest in bronze was carried off by King Dagobert from the Church of St. Hilary on raiding Poitiers, and given to his newly founded Abbey of St. Denis. In England there are scarcely any previous to the fifteenth century. Of the many eagle-type ones are those at Holy Rood, South Hampton; St. Margaret, King's Lynn; Holy Trinity, Coventry; St. Peter, Oundle; St. Gregory, Norwich (1496); and Chipping Campden (page 98). While there are many variations of the eagle in Belgium, there are but few in France or Germany, and scarcely any in Italy. By way of fonts, there may not be more than fifty survivors in all of Europe, according to Perry. Only in the Lowlands and Germany are they to be found. As a rule they are not particularly architectural, often with heavy bases if turned, as at Linköping, or with archaic figures as at Hildesheim. Those later than the thirteenth century became more architectural than preceeding ones, often having an octagonal bowl resting on arcaded figures. A splendidly designed circular one exists at St. Sebaldskirche, Hildesheim, with a double arcade and four figures at the axes.

FIG. 3.—BRONZE DOOR FROM AN EGYPTIAN MOSQUE, INLAID WITH GOLD AND SILVER. (FOURTEENTH CENTURY)

FIG. 4.—DIABUTSU, OR GREAT BRONZE BUDDHA OF KAMAKURA, JAPAN, EXTREME IN SCALE FOR AN ORIENTAL BRONZE. (CAST IN 1252 BY OYO GOROYÉMON)

FIG. 5.—GREEK MIRROR OF BRONZE, NOW IN NATIONAL MUSEUM, ATHENS. (FIFTH OR FOURTH CENTURY B. C.)

ITALY

The glamour of the Italian thirteenth- and fourteenth-century bronzes is apt to obscure the absence of any of importance in the preceeding millenium when the preëminence established by the Romans was relinquished to Byzantine, French and German craftsmen. From the decadence of the Roman Empire until the twelfth century Italy produced practically no bronze. Sculpture in Rome declined under the Christian emperors, and while some bronzes were produced for both the palaces of the nobility and the churches, as *baldacchinos* and sarcóphagi, but little still remains. The catacombs have yielded up some lamps, crosses, and emblems of the faith, but nothing of any great architectural significance. The only surviving bronze of importance is the much revered seated figure of St. Peter in St. Peter's, Rome, which was made in 453 by order of Leo I (The Great); the original chair was of marble, the present bronze one dates from the fifteenth century. During the troublesome centuries for Rome following the subdivision into the two empires, Byzantium rulers displayed no interest in the welfare of Rome. The visit of Constans II for twelve days in 663 was no exception. He stripped the city of such bronze as was valuable, including the bronze tiles of the Pantheon, and loaded them on a ship which unfortunately was either wrecked or fell into the hands of the Saracens.

With the decreasing importance of Rome as capital of the Western Empire, Constantinople, as head of the Eastern, encouraged and attracted artists to carry on the bronze traditions there. In 543 Justinian ordered the doors for St. Sophia. The wood structure of 4 or 5 inches in thickness was overlaid with bronze plates, which varied from ¼ to ½ inch in thickness, having panels enriched by running ornament and frets, as well as monograms and inscriptions in silver niello; they were swung on pivots let into top and bottom rails at the jambs. By the seventh century the Byzantian influence, emanating from Constantinople and extending into Italy, had completely replaced all vestige of the Classic as carried on in the Early Christian manner. In neither the Eastern nor the Western Empire were there many bronze castings of importance, excepting the doors of St. Sophia and several now in St. Mark's (cast in Constantinople), although there are some thrones, church reliquaries, lamps, and the like still re-

maining. A column covered by bronze plates and surmounted by an equestrian statue of himself (30 feet high over all), ordered by Justinian, was not melted down until the sixteenth century. After the sixth century the scene of bronze casting shifted from Constantinople to France and Germany, and not until the eleventh was there a revival of the craft here.

After the beginning of the eleventh century, bronze again appears in Italian architecture, following a lapse of nearly a thousand years. Doors were the main expression, and these may be divided into three classes previous to those for the Florence Baptistry: the group cast by Staurachios (or Staurontius) at Constantinople for the Pantaleone family of Amalfi; other imported ones, as at San Zeno at Verona (perhaps from Germany); and those of Italian artists from the south. These are all in the so-called Byzantine or Romanesque manner, and are followed by the Florence Baptistry doors, first those by Andrea Pisano in 1330, in the transitional Gothic-Renaissance style, and then by the purely Renaissance series, best represented by Ghiberti's.

The reappearance of bronze in eleventh-and twelfth-century Italian architecture is marked by the patronage of the church and the Pantaleone family of Amalfi, the formation of schools, and the emigration of Greek founders from Constantinople. Writers of the period express a high regard for the craftsmanship of the Saracens, then located in Sicily, and there was at times a strong admixture of the Saracenic strain in the dominating Byzantine-Romanesque design of the time. Occasionally the influence of the antique asserted itself as strongly as though there were no Byzantine style, as in the doors of the Benevento Duomo. The sum total of these influences enriched southern Italy by about twenty sets of bronze church doors—a greater number of this period in fact, than is possessed by the remainder of Europe combined. In general the doors of these two centuries were constructed on wood cores, with bronze plates nailed or bolted on. In many of the extant examples it is evident from the appearance of the panels that the wood behind has shrunk, sagged or rotted. Bronze ornament was either cast, or beaten out in *repoussé* work. Decoration took the form of either bas-relief, or niello, i. e., incising lines and filling them usually with a black sulphuric compound or sometimes silver. At Monte Cassino the possessions of the abbey in 1067 were written on the doors with the precious metal in this fashion.

Niccolò Pisano (c. 1200–'80) and his son Giovanni (1250–1328) sowed the seeds of the Renaissance, and subsequent to their times bronze history in Italy becomes largely a matter of successive biographies. The school founded by them included Andrea Pisano da Pontedera, son of Ugolino di Nino (1270–1330), an obscure goldsmith who received the commission to execute the first doors of the Florence Baptistry. These are divided into panels

FIG. 6.—BRONZE ITALIAN ARMOR OF THE SIXTEENTH CENTURY

depicting the life of St. John, are indicative of the transitional Gothic-Renaissance spirit, and are contained within the favorite Florentine shape of a quatrefoil intersected by a square (page 50). Andrea Pisano worked under Giovanni, later went to Venice where he learned the Byzantine technique of bronze casting, and became renowned as the best bronze sculptor of his day in Italy. He is known for the bronze crucifix made for Clement V, who presented it to his friend Giotto. His most celebrated work, the south doors of the Florence Baptistry, were originally on the east side facing the Duomo; they were subsequently surmounted by a rich frieze which was modeled and partly worked by Lorenzo Ghiberti, and, after his death, completed by his son Vittorio and followers.

In the entire history of architectural bronze,

probably no name is as deserving of immortality as that of Lorenzo Ghiberti (1378–1455) for his masterly Baptistry doors (pages 52–57). The story of his victory over Brunelleschi in the competition of the trial panel of the Sacrifice of Abraham, is too well known to bear repetition. It is significant that he spent fifty years on the two sets of Baptistry doors. When they are rightly appraised as being the finest achievements of their kind, and the *finesse* of the detail and surfacing is fully appreciated, it should be borne in mind that it is because the master sculptor understood his metal, perceived the modeling appropriate to it, and realized the necessity for the refinement of cast detail. The first set of doors took twenty-one years to finish, even with the aid of twenty artists. After completion they were gilded, but it is doubtful if this was commendable; confined to mouldings, there might have been some virtue in the contrast of colors.

Donatello or Donato, son of Niccolò di Betti Bardi (1386–1466), dispelled the last vestiges of the Gothic, and imbued bas-reliefs with greater scope. Instead of the usual uniformly projecting masses, he created an impressionistic effect of movement and distance by the perspective of the architecture and the lessening projection of receding figures. Among his famed bronze bas-reliefs are the Sienese font, the altar of Sant' Antonio at Padua, and the two pulpits of San Lorenzo at Florence. His equestrian statue of Gattamelata at Padua (1453) was one of the first great bronzes cast in the Italian Renaissance.

Lucca della Robbia (1399? or 1400?–1482) is best known for his glazed terra-cotta, but he is partially responsible for one notable bronze work: the doors to the new Sacristy of the Duomo at Florence (1446–'67), in conjunction with Michelozzo and Maso di Bartolomeo (page 51).

Among the better known of Donatello's pupils was Antonio Averulino, called Filarete (1431–'84), who, with the assistance of Simone, executed the main doors to St. Peter's, Rome. To the same school is attributed (and chiefly to Simone with some doubt), the exquisite Prato grille (pages 64–65), screening the Chapel of the Sacred Girdle (*Cingolo*) in the Cathedral.

The most gifted of Donatello's pupils was Andrea Cione di Michele, called Verrocchio (1435–'88). While he is known for no strictly architectural bronze, at least three of his works are too famed to be omitted: the horse of the

Colleoni equestrian statue at Venice (the figure was modeled by Alessandro Leopardi), the fountain in the Palazzo Vecchio courtyard, and the famous David in the Bargello collection, the latter two being in Florence.

Nothing which Michael Angelo Buonarroti (1475–1564) executed in bronze still remains.

Benvenuto Cellini (1500–'71) spent his early life as a goldsmith in Florence and Rome, and later went to Paris. Not only most of his executed bronzes remain, but also the colorful accounts of his experiences. His bronzes approach being architectural no closer than some bas-reliefs, as the "Nymph of Fontainebleau." His best-known sculpture in bronze is Perseus and the Medusa. In his account of pouring the figure of Perseus in a single casting, he describes his becoming ill with a fever just as everything was in readiness to pour; he was forced to bed and in the midst of great agony a message was brought him, "Past earthly remedy, your work is ruined." In spite of his illness he rushed to the scene and had more tin and wood added, but the additional forced heat caused the furnace to burst. The fissure was plugged up and in the absence of needed tin, "dishes, plates, bowls, and two-hundred pieces of his table service" were thrown in, and there was consequently sufficient metal to fill the mould. The statue has been much admired since its completion in April of 1554.

Giovanni da Bologna, or Giambologna, (Jean de Boullogne of Douai, 1524–1628), is renowned principally for the fountain at Bologna, on which he worked for three years. The base is marble, surmounted by bronze sirens, armorial shields and a crowning figure of Neptune 9 feet high. Subsequently he executed a number of minor bronzes, but in 1595 completed his last great work, the bronze doors for the Cathedral of Pisa, to replace those of Bonanno which were destroyed by the fire of that year. Unfortunately their inferiority is evident in comparison with those executed two centuries before (pages 46 and 49).

Giovanni Lorenzo Bernini (1589–1680) gave the craft a new but momentary impetus by the exercise of *tour-de-force* creations. His *baldacchino* over the high altar at St. Peter's is of bronze except for certain small passages of gold, and is representative of his manner. In 1627

he erected a huge statue of San Carlo Borromeo, 75 feet high on a forty foot pedestal, overlooking Lago Maggiore just north of Arona. The head, feet, and hands are of cast bronze,

FIG. 7.—ITALIAN PAX OF ABOUT 1490 IN ORIGINAL GILT METAL MOUNTING

The bronze relief in the centre is attributed to Sandro Botticelli; the plinth has three niello plaques; the mounting of chiselled bronze has silver filigree work

but the remainder is of copper plates overlaid on a masonry core.

During the eighteenth and nineteenth centuries no architectural or sculptural bronze of importance was executed. It is to be hoped that the remarkable realization of latent nationalistic and artistic power, awakened since the World War, will shortly begin to shape its record in bronze comparable to the best Italian precedent.

FRANCE

The Merovingian dynasty (481–752) is responsible for a certain amount of existing bronze, but its history is so sketchy and its examples so few, that extant architectural bronze in France may better be said to have begun with the Aix-la-Chapelle doors. St. Eloy (Eloi), 588–659, Master of the Mint under Dagobert, was traditionally famed for his skill in metals by the time he was thirty, and while his name is associated with the Chair of Dagobert (Fig. 8), some authorities believe parts

FIG. 8.—BRONZE OR BRASS CHAIR OF DAGOBERT, ATTRIBUTED TO ST. ELOY AND SUGER

of the bronze gilt chair to be Roman. It may simply be a copy of a Roman curule chair, the lower part of it surviving from the Merovingian dynasty, but certainly added to and completed in the twelfth century by Suger, Abbot of St. Denis (1082–1152), Chancellor to Louis VI and VII. Merovingian bronze artists were apparently more interested in enriching portions of weapons, buckles, and ornaments of dress with bronze, than buildings.

The first bronze in France of architectural importance dates from the ninth century, when Charlemagne (son of Charles Martel, who founded the second Frankish dynasty, the Carlovingian, 752–987), set about to cast the doors for the Cathedral of Aix-la-Chapelle about 804. Because nothing of the kind had

been accomplished since the reign of Justinian at Constantinople, Charlemagne's task was both difficult and novel, and it is of some interest where he obtained the necessary technical information. It is thought that he may have seen the bronze doors which Pope Adrian had brought from Perugia before the ones for the Cathedral at Aix-la-Chapelle were executed. The latter consist of two leaves, are divided into panels with decorated mouldings, have lions' heads with rings for handles, surrounded by a palmette, and are somewhat Etruscan in feeling. The pseudo-classic influence of Charlemagne affected German bronze craft two centuries later in its revival under Bishop Bernard of Hildesheim.

In the tenth and eleventh centuries, when the Byzantine strongly colored German art in bronze, it influenced the Mosan towns (valley of the river Meuse), France and England only superficially. At the close of the tenth century the bronze craft was fostered by the Benedictine monasteries, and the traditions were preserved in the work by the monk Theophilus in the early eleventh. For three centuries *dinanderie* (the making of church and domestic works in copper and its alloys) flourished in the Mosan towns, and, in the internecine struggles which ensued, tradesmen and craftsmen spread the knowledge of bronze technique as they were scattered over Flanders and Brabant. Because of the popular belief that the world would come to an end at the close of the tenth century, many beautiful but small gifts in metal work were given to the church; after safely passing the millennium mark the tendency was to create works of art on a grander scale. It is of interest that the *cire perdue* method of casting was used at this time.

The most important figure in the bronze revival of the twelfth century is Suger, already referred to in conjunction with Dagobert's chair. In 1140 he introduced in his Abbey of St. Denis the first bronze doors in France since those at Aix-la-Chapelle. These were of gilt bronze, decorated by bas-reliefs representing historical aspects of the Passion, Resurrection, and Ascension in *rilievo*. The ones at Augsburg Cathedral (1070?, 1080?) are very similar. Although the doors of St. Denis were in existence until 1706, nothing now remains by Suger except the Dagobert chair. Architecturally it is of interest that some authorities point to his portion of the Abbey as marking the beginning of Gothic tendencies.

But little of thirteenth-century bronze remains, or, for that matter, only very little may ever have existed. The nearest approach to architectural bronze during this period are the many figures or statues on tombs. Amiens Cathedral has two notable ones commemorating two of its bishops, Everard de Fouilloy (died 1222) and Geoffrey d'Eu (died 1236). The figures are cast in high relief on a slab supported at the angles and sides by six lions. Limoges artists became prominent at this time in their particular forte of forming beaten copper over wood cores and inlaying it with precious stones, metals, and enamel, but as nearly as can be determined they executed no cast bronze of any great size.

During the period of the Gothic ascendancy bronze was but little used, and not until the Renaissance did its employment in architecture become important. The transition from one style to the other was not violent but gradual. Francis I invited the foremost artists of Italy to come to France, among whom were Da Vinci and Cellini. The latter remained four years, but executed no bronze which is known; on incurring the ill will of the king

FIG. 9.—EMPIRE EWER OF GILT BRONZE. (EARLY NINETEENTH CENTURY)

and Madame d'Estampes, he returned to Italy.

In general the tendency after the Renaissance was to employ bronze on a small scale, as for clock cases, furniture mountings, candelabra, candlesticks, mountings for marble vases, etc. Domestic vessels were fashioned from *repoussé* bronze, often of most exquisite design and workmanship. During the seventeenth, eighteenth, and beginning of the nineteenth centuries, what was wanting in large architectural bronzes is compensated for by the perfection of the lesser ones, as those enumerated above. Particularly in the Directoire and Empire periods, the *finesse* of the detail and perfection of the technique have scarcely ever been equalled and probably never surpassed (pages 67, 68, and 175).

Since the vast majority of French bronzes, partly or entirely architectural, have been on a small scale and easily looted or destroyed, there is not only a dearth of examples of the Gothic period, but even of the Renaissance. Huguenot troubles, internal and external wars, iconoclasm, and at one time the opinion that Gothic art was "barbaric," ruinously despoiled the enormous wealth of artistic treasures which otherwise would record the enviable history of French bronzes and craftsmanship.

GERMANY

The history of bronze in Germany is unique in its origin. Not because of commercial supremacy or military triumphs were the archaic and feeble attempts previous to the end of the tenth century converted into a far-reaching awakening, but because of a woman. Theophano, wife of King Otho and daughter of Romanus II (the Byzantine emperor), surrounded herself by persons skilled in the arts, and is directly responsible for the revival in the metallic crafts. Naturally, since the artists were Byzantine, the bronze designs and casting technique frankly displayed their origin. Again Aix-la-Chapelle became the centre of the bronze activity, having first come into such importance two centuries earlier when Charlemagne had

the doors for the Cathedral cast in bronze.

In the revival of the bronze craft at the end of the tenth century and early eleventh, two of the most important figures are the Archbishop Willigis of Mainz, who ordered the doors for his cathedral in 998 (the oldest extant ones after those for Aix-la-Chapelle, and which survived the fire of the Cathedral), and Bishop Bernard of Hildesheim. The latter was himself skilled in the bronze craft, it is thought, and may have done more than to "order" the bronze doors for St. Michael's, which have since been hung on the Cathedral of Hildesheim (page 16). He is responsible for the "Christussäule" at Hildesheim (1022), a monumental column of bronze which is strongly

FIGS. 10 AND 11.—LEFT AND RIGHT LEAVES OF TWO
PAIRS OF BRONZE DOORS. (ELEVENTH CENTURY)

Hildesheim Cathedral   Gnesen Cathedral

quaries, crucifixes, monstrances, and smaller
church appurtenances were often of gilt bronze.
The Cathedral of Goslar has a celebrated bronze
altar inlaid with jewels. Bronze doors were
cast for the Cathedral at Gnesen, as well as
for that of Augsburg (page 17). The date for
the latter is variously given, but is probably
from about 1070 to 1080; from the curious
spacing of the narrow panels, which seem to
have no good reason for being so when compared with the wider ones, it is thought to have
undergone alterations at a later date.

In the twelfth and thirteenth centuries there
were fewer large monumental examples of
bronze, but the products of the crafts were
more diversified and numerous than in the
previous period. Modeling became superior in
its feeling for line, purity, and grace but still
left much to be desired. The Romanesque
style was assimilated and given an independent
and naturalistic flavor, yet the majority of
bronzes were too often inclined to be archaic
and crude. In 1165 Frederick Barbarossa made
one of his infrequent trips to Germany and
opened the tomb of Charlemagne; the jewelry,
relics, etc., had an important influence upon
design. Fortnum points out that "admirable
reliquaries and other church objects, with figures of apostles, etc., in copper or bronze gilt,
as candelabra, ewers, etc., were made." Among
important church bronzes are the Shrine of the
Virgin, Cathedral of Aix-la-Chapelle, and the
bronze font in the Würzburg Cathedral by
Eckhard of Worms (1279), modeled in the
Gothic manner and having eight divisions depicting scenes from the life of Christ.

Bronze doors have ever been the chief employment for the metal, architecturally, yet
from the close of the twelfth century until the
nineteenth only an occasional one was cast in
Germany. The fourteenth century did not
make any startling contribution in the realm
of bronze. By the mid-century the chief centres at Nuremberg and Augsburg crystallized
modeling into a new style which radiated to
other parts of the country; figures were short
and of bad proportions, features were exaggerated, hair was wig-like, and the draperies
were clumsy. By the end of the century, however, there seemed to be steady progress made
in the technique of casting. A series of bronze
fonts was begun. "Monumental brasses," with
the figure engraved in outline for use over
tombs, were introduced but soon went out of
fashion and were supplanted by low-relief fig-

reminiscent of those of Trajan and Aurelian in
Rome. The existing shaft is 15 feet high, but
the capital and surmounting cross have disappeared; twenty-eight or -nine tableaux from
the life of Christ are arranged spirally around
the shaft. Two bronze candlesticks of Hildesheim are also ascribed to the bishop. If these
two churchmen did not actually possess knowledge of the craft, they at least were enthusiastic patrons and an excess of credit cannot
be accorded them.

The eleventh century was an eventful one
in German bronze, following the propitious
impetus generated at the beginning of the century by the Bishops Bernard and Willigis. Not
only was bronze cast and chiselled ("chased"
in the modern sense), but it also was wrought,
especially at Augsburg. Elaborate doors, gates,
and furniture were fashioned for churches; reli-

ures. During the thirteenth and fourteenth centuries bronze was but rarely used in monumental sculptures, as was also the case in France at this time. One of the few remarkable ones is the small equestrian statue of St. George at Prague, a fountain-figure in the second court of the Royal Palace, by Martin and Georg Klausenburg (1373); the horse was restored in 1562, according to Baedeker. In the Cologne Cathedral there is a good example of the bronze work of the period in the tomb of Archbishop Conrad von Hochstaden (died 1261; monument probably after 1322).

The fifteenth and sixteenth centuries are not represented by numerous architectural bronzes. Two of the early sixteenth are of preëminent importance in German art, and atone in a measure for the absence of numerous lesser ones. Peter Vischer and his five sons executed the shrine to St. Sebald in the church bearing the saint's name in Nuremberg (1508-'19). While it is not to be compared, from an artistic standpoint, with Italian bronzes such as those by Donatello, yet it is well cast, is indicative of the trend in the painstaking German sculpture in the early part of the sixteenth century, and shows the blending of the traditional manner with that of the local "humanists." The silver sarcophagus is covered by a canopy surmounted by three domes, and is supported by a platform resting on twelve snails. The other monument of equal or perhaps greater importance is one to Emperor Maximilian I in the Hofkirche or Franciscan Church of Innsbruck, erected about the same time as the Sebald shrine. The court-painter, Gilg Sesselschreiber, designed the monument and superintended its execution (1508-'18), until Stephen Godl succeeded him. The centre sarcophagus of marble is surrounded by 28 statues between round shafts. The statues are not of uniform quality; they form a double row around the sarcophagus, and are about 8 feet in height. The elaboration of details and the qualities of the casting are the chief virtues of the monument, since neither the conception nor the modeling is particularly admirable or imaginative. Nationalistic traits were continued until the mid-century, but subsequently the imitations of Michael Angelo became more and more numerous. The Thirty Years' War, which blighted all branches of art, paralyzed the bronze craft as well.

The seventeenth century and early eighteenth are marked by no outstanding architectural accomplishments. The nearest approach

FIG. 12.—BRONZE DOORS, AUGSBURG CATHEDRAL. (1070 OR 1080?)

are two statues, one of Frederick III set up in Königsberg, modeled by Andreas Schluter (1697) and cast by Jacobi; another, an equestrian statue, was cast by the same craftsman of the Great Elector in 1700, and erected in 1703 on a Berlin bridge. Typical German traditions, which had succumbed to Italian tradition during the last half of the sixteenth century, also fell victim to the contagious French influence from Louis XIV (1643-1715) until well after the Empire style had established itself in the nineteenth century.

During the nineteenth century Germany carried casting to a point of technical perfection which quite overshadowed the importance of taste in the modeling. The application of zinc to ornamental casting was experimented with, and its immediate substitution for bronze was urged in 1840. Small bronzes were produced in quantity and were in demand by the public, but no exceptionally meritorious architectural achievements were produced.

ENGLAND

The history of bronze in England is so unimportant architecturally as to be practically negligible. In view of the fact that her wrought iron was individualistic in design, her lead work unsurpassed in quantity and quality, and her brass tomb-plates so popular and carefully engraved as to produce condensed provincial records of the times, it is perplexing why bronze was not a favorite material and why modeling was not suitable in character.

The earliest bronzes in England are of Saxon craftsmanship, strongly influenced by Scandinavian and Celtic precedents, particularly the former, and remarkable for "interlacing serpentine folds with zoomorphic terminations." In Ireland bronze was cast at least as early as the ninth century, judging from an inscription on a celebrated bell of Armagh—one of a series to supersede the type with rivetted iron plates. The first personal coloring lent to the history of English bronze is in the "fostering care of Athelstane, and in the guidance and example of St. Dunstan" (924–'88). The latter was the son of a west Saxon noble, who founded the Benedictine order in England providing for the encouragement of the monks in working at the arts, and who eventually became Archbishop of Canterbury. He studied the Charlemagne bronze work at Aix-la-Chapelle and witnessed the beginning of the bronze revival in Germany. Nothing cast by St. Dunstan is known to have survived.

Bronze was but rarely employed except for effigies. It was used on a small scale and to a limited extent for construction purposes in the early thirteenth century. At Salisbury Cathedral it occurs in small rings which tie the isolated shafts to central columns of the great piers, and there is a moulded abacus on the central pier of the west entrance. Knockers and sanctuary rings were sometimes

FIG. 13.—INSIDE OF BRONZE DOOR, BEVERLEY MINSTER, ENGLAND

cast from it. The "Gloucester candlestick" is of doubtful origin, and may possibly be German. Of the many bronze shrines which once existed, practically nothing survives.

The casting of effigies was introduced by the Plantagenet kings, the first being of Henry III (died 1272) and his queen, Eleanor (died 1291); these were of bronze gilt cast by William Torell (also Torel) in 1391, and are in Westminster Abbey. Both technique and modeling are commendable, although neither is in the round. The elaborate cast and gilt bronze effigy of Edward, the Black Prince (died 1376), is in Canterbury Cathedral. Another royal effigy was that cast for Edward III (died 1377). In 1394 the mould was made for the figures of Richard II (reigned 1377–'99) and his queen, Anne of Bohemia, and a contract made for gilt images with Godfrey and Nicholas Broker, London coppersmiths. During the reign of the House of Plantagenet (mid-twelfth to beginning of fifteenth century), the activity of the bronze craft bore some semblance to that in other parts of Europe, but during the Wars of the Roses it languished and by the time of the accession of the Tudors (1485), the craft seemed practically dead. Only a few monuments of the sixteenth century are of importance: the mortuary chests above the screens of the presbytery in Winchester Cathedral, set up by Bishop Fox (1500–'28) to contain the remains of Canute, William Rufus and some early bishops; the bronze double-sarcophagus and figures of Edward VII (died 1509) and his wife, Elizabeth of York, modeled by Torregiano; and the brass gates of the Henry VII Chapel, Westminster Abbey (1505). The *cire perdue* process was generally employed.

The "monumental brasses," let into the top stone slab of tombs, are treated separately under the chapter on "Brass" (pages 95–96).

BELGIUM

Ever since the twelfth century the towns of Liège and Namur have been noted for the excellence of their manufacture of brasses and bronzes, particularly in such forms as fonts and their covers, sconces, candelabra, lecterns, "monumental brasses," and effigies. Belgian bronze practically begins with the font in St. Barthélemy, Liège, cast in 1112 by Lambert Patras of Dinant, and the so-called censer of Lille, at the beginning of the twelfth century; both are sometimes attributed to Reguier of Huy, and are of cast metal "sculptured and engraved." In the early thirteenth century a monk, Hugh de Walcourt, a prolific and artistic worker in bronze, cast among other works a reliquary-monstrance "richly carved, gilt and adorned with niello," which supposedly contains one of the ribs of St. Peter. In the fifteenth century several outstanding monuments bear mentioning: two fine pieces of work by William le Fevre, a lectern in the Church of St. Gislain near Mons (1472), a font at Hal, and, perhaps most famous of all, two life-sized recumbent figures in gilt bronze of Charles the Bold (died 1477) and his daughter, Mary of Burgundy (died 1482), wife of the Emperor Maximilian. These are now in a side chapel, (but were once in the choir) of Notre Dame in Bruges, the effigy of the daughter being by Pieter de Beckere, a Brussels goldsmith (made 1495–1502), and that of her father by Jacob Jongelincx and J. Aerts from designs by M. Gheeraerts, erected in 1559 by Philip II who was a descendant of Charles the Bold.

SPAIN

While not much native bronze was produced in Spain prior to the sixteenth century, subsequently the metal seemed to assimilate certain Moorish tendencies. In the doors of Toledo (1337), Cordova (1377), and Seville, Moorish precedent is much in evidence; the swarthy craftsmen had long used a hard alloy of copper and tin, decorating it with inlaid silver wire or silver sheets cut in conventional patterns. Not many examples remain, unfortunately, due partly to the religious hate of anything "infidel." Bronze altars with enamel inlay were most likely imported from Limoges, as those at San Esteban, Salamanca, and San Miguel de Excelsis, Navarre.

Although iron was the particular favorite of the metal craftsmen of the sixteenth century, there are a few outstanding exceptions in bronze. Among these are: the pulpits on both sides of the high altar at Santiago, with gilt reliefs by Juan Celma (1563); the bronze candelabrum, Seville; a figure of Faith serving as the weather-vane on the Giralda, Seville (14 feet high and weighing about one and a quarter tons, 1568); the main pillars of the *coro*, and one of three reading desks (called *El Aguila*, from the bronze eagle with outstretched wings), the latter by Vicente Salinas (1646), both being in Toledo Cathedral; and the grille, mostly bronze, at the burial chapel of Gabriel de Zaporta in the old Cathedral of Saragossa (1579). An exception to the craftsmen who preferred iron to bronze was Francisco de Villalpando. When he won the competition for the *capilla mayor* grille of the Toledo Cathedral (1540–'48) he executed it partly in bronze. He is also responsible for the gilt bronze pulpits, the bronze doors with admirable bas-reliefs of the Puerta de los Leones (1545–'50), the font, and the rail to the Altar of the Virgin in the *coro* (1551–'64), all in the Toledo Cathedral, and in his native town, Palencia, the choir screens of the Cathedral (1522?, also given as 1555).

After the middle of the sixteenth century when Spanish prosperity and commercial domination declined, the effect upon the metal crafts was immediate. Only occasional works were created in iron, the popular medium, while in the less favored bronze practically nothing was cast.

FIG. 14.—BRONZE STATUE, "DIANA," BY PAUL MANSHIP

A brilliant example of bronze-understanding by the sculptor,
for it is impossible to conceive this statue in any other material

BRONZE: CRAFTSMANSHIP

THE ESSENTIALS OF CASTING

THE process of bronze casting in the grand old days when the world was youthful was not much different from the process to-day. There have been muscle-saving devices developed, such as the travelling crane, chain blocks, compressed air (from the foreman and otherwise), electrical and steam power, etc., but a good casting is as much dependent upon the human factor now as then. Strangely enough, even the composition of the material has undergone no radical departures from the initial concoction. Bronze Age relics found at the bottom of the Swiss lakes and in certain European caverns contain 90 per cent copper and 10 per cent tin. Recent United States Government specifications have approved the same proportion of copper, but only 7 per cent of tin and 3 per cent zinc. A permissible Government change recently has been to subtract 1 per cent of copper and substitute lead. This, of course, refers to ornamental bronze, such as composes statues, doors, counter-screens, pilasters, and other like architectural forms. The formula for the well-known Versailles bronzes, much admired for their patina (by the Keller brothers), was: copper 91.6 per cent, zinc 5.33, tin 1.7, and lead 1.37.

As far as the architect is concerned, after the client has been persuaded into signing on the dotted line and the bronze contractor has been notified of this fact, the first step is for the modeler to begin his models. When these have been prepared in clay, altered to meet the architect's approval, and cast in plaster, they are sent to the bronze foundry as the initial step toward the casting process. At this point it may be in order to suggest that the architect in his modeling specifications include the provision that all models be properly backed, so that they will not be damaged at the foundry when the moulds are made. It is a good precaution to take, or there may ensue one of those interesting but seldom fruitful wars between modeler and foundry as to who should do the backing. Assuming, however, that your bronze man is a good-natured fellow, accustomed to swallowing his pride at this game, and that he

accepts the models as they come from the modeler, let us continue.

The preliminary job on which the bronze contractor has been working whilst the modeler made merry in clay is to prepare complete working drawings from the architect's details. As a rule the latter are complete enough where there is straight and easy sailing, but inadequate where there are some tough and dubious corners to turn. "The shop drawings will take care of that" is the architect's slogan too often where acceleration is desired, causing lost time and motion for both the foundry and the architect's office; eventually the latter must make final decision by working out the ambiguous and intricate conditions. For example, the following diagram (Figure 15) indicates a prob-

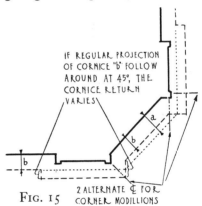

IF REGULAR PROJECTION OF CORNICE "b" FOLLOW AROUND AT 45°, THE CORNICE RETURN VARIES

FIG. 15   2 ALTERNATE ℄ FOR CORNER MODILLIONS

lem which might arise on a counter-screen detail. For one thing, unless the modeler took his detail at the corner, there is nothing to give any indication as to what the intersection of ornament is to be. The bronze draftsmen can do intersections of the mouldings readily enough, but unless the architect's propensities are known, they will be doubtful whether he will want a dentil overlapping the break on the corner, or prefer to have one on each side; whether he prefers a modillion at right angles to the facia, or would rather see the modillion centre on the line of intersection. More important still, the bronze draftsmen will have no way of determining whether the projection of the cornice at *a* on the 45-degree corner should be the same as at *b*; if so, it means a greater break in the cornice than was shown on the architect's drawings. This latter condition arises frequently, and after the bronze is erected the architect cannot understand why the bronze contractor did not have the sense to make the same cornice projection all around. After all, even the best bronze contractor makes no claim to clairvoyance and agrees to furnish none.

Assuming that the shop drawings have received their final red check-marks and rubber stamps, and the models have arrived from the modeler's properly backed, the next thing in order is the making of the inside and outside sand "cores," which, when fitted together in a so-called "flask," will allow an empty space between them into which the molten bronze will be poured. This can be more easily explained by taking a concrete case of the casting of a bust, as diagrammed in Figures 17 and 18. *A*, the frame (termed a "flask" for some peculiar reason), confines the sculptor's model, *B*, as well as the sand packed inside and outside of it, *D* and *H*. The point previously taken concerning a model's being well backed may be clarified by noticing, if the interior of the head or shoulders were not of sound thickness, that when the sand, *D*, is rammed around it, the model might easily cave in, much to every one's consternation. The highly specialized work at this juncture is the forming of the blocks of sand termed "cores" at *D* in Figures 17 and 18. These must be carefully fitted around the cast in such a manner that they can be lifted out without damage to themselves. In the event of "undercutting" this may necessitate several "cores," as indicated in Figure 16. It takes a steady hand and long experience to know which cores to build up first and what shape they had best take. The moulder employs a variety of attractive spoons, rammers and other tools to guide the sand where it should go, and to pack it firmly to form a unified chunk.

Referring again to Figures 17 and 18, the next operation on the bust after outside cores are made is to give it some brains plus etceteras, or, technically speaking, an inner core

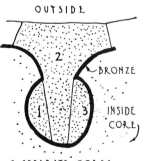

OUTSIDE

2

BRONZE

1 3

INSIDE CORE

3 SEPARATE CORES
1 & 3 PLACED IN POSITION FIRST, # 2 LAST.

FIG. 16

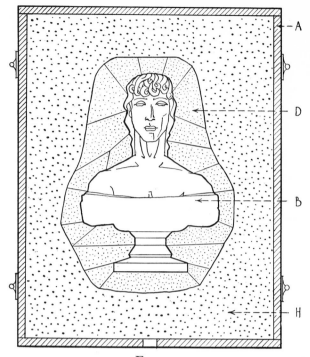

FIG. 17

A.—Iron frames called "flasks."
B.—Sculptor's plaster model of a portrait bust.
D.—Separate blocks of moulding sand called "cores."
H.—Outer sand backing or outer envelope of the mould.

indicated by *E*. The culmination of all these processes is to form a space into which the metal can flow so as to produce a bronze shell about $\frac{1}{8}$ to $\frac{1}{4}$ of an inch thick, the outside of which will be an exact replica of the sculptor's model. The formation of the aggregate sand blocks already described will form the outer confine for the molten metal, and what remains to be made is an inner core which will be about $\frac{1}{8}$ to $\frac{1}{4}$ of an inch smaller all around than the sculptor's model. This is achieved by making a duplicate of the model in sand, reinforced by supports like the iron bars, *F*, then shaving down the surface equally all over by approximately $\frac{1}{4}$ of an inch—in other words cutting away a coating of sand to correspond to the thickness which the metal will have when poured, shown by *J* (unshaded portion). The inner core thus fashioned is suspended in the flask as the outer cores are carefully packed around it in their respective places, and the operation is then almost advanced to the pouring stage. All that remains is the forming of "gates" and "vents," which are merely grooves, the former for letting the metal in, and the latter for letting air and gases out. These are made in *H*, the outer sand backing, after the cores have been perfectly fitted. *G*

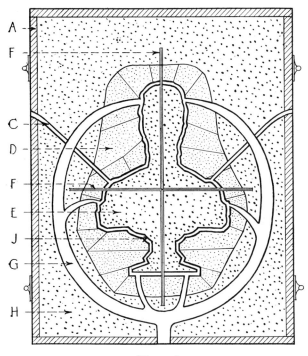

FIG. 18

A.—Iron frames called "flasks."
C.—Vents in mould for the escape of gases generated by contact
        of molten metal with the sand.
D.—Separate blocks of moulding sand called "cores."
E.—Inner sand core.
F.—Iron bars which support the inner sand core *E.*
G.—Feeding channels through which the molten metal is carried
        to all parts of the mould (shown unshaded).
H.—Outer sand backing or outer envelope of the mould.
J.—Space between inner and outer sand cores, which when filled
        with molten bronze (unshaded portion), forms the
        bronze cast.

village of Fontenay-aux-Roses on the out-skirts of Paris. It comes from the one and only pit of its kind, is considered to have no equal, and is of such value that any small boy might well feel driven to digging up his back yard in hopes of discovering a similar product which would be sufficiently valuable to humble Ford himself. In being used for cores this French sand is packed moist, and when judged to fit perfectly with its neighbors and the model, is dried out in an oven; its contraction is practically negligible. It is so smooth that when fingered moist it seems more like clay than sand. It is so valuable that when its job on one cast is over, it is repulverized, sifted, and used over again, but not for facing directly against the model.

The foregoing description deals with the making of a mould for ornament in heavy re-lief or statues in bronze, which, because of the undercutting, necessitates the sand cores be-ing lifted from the model as described above, instead of the model from the sand. This latter method can be employed for all flat work where there is no undercutting, as in most doors, pi-lasters, cornices, etc. Figure 19 illustrates this point. Standing upright at the right in the photograph is Daniel Chester French's model for one of the Boston Public Library doors. The imprint of it is seen on the mould for the front of the door, while the mould in the fore-ground for its reverse side is simply panelled. Figure 20 illustrates the same type of mould on a smaller scale. In case there is consider-able repetition of units to be cast for such architectural forms as door rosettes, counter-screen ornaments, etc., a "pattern" may be made of wood or metal, whichever may best suit the condition. In principle these serve the same purpose as the plaster models described, and, if undercut, would have cores built around them to form a mould in the same manner.

For castings with many small undercuts which would necessitate numberless sand cores, or difficult bar sections as the marginal diagram overleaf, another process known as the *cire per-due* or "lost wax" method is employed. It was used by the ancients and is not so secret but that any interested person can read about it at length, and not, as some would have one believe, shrouded in dead men's trade secrets. Briefly described it consists of making a sand model slightly smaller than the desired casting —in fact, smaller all over by the thickness which it is desired that the metal should have;

in Figure 18 represents the feeding channels or "gates" through which the molten metal will flow; these are simply made by cutting away the sand before it is baked with a spoon-like tool and painting the sand surface with "black lead" so as to prevent the sand from washing, which might otherwise offer resistance to the flow of the metal. Smaller grooves, as at *C*, are cut from the space to be filled with the metal, *J*, out to the air, so that collecting gases and dislodged air may have a means of escape. The various parts are assembled for a trial fit and then removed, to be dried or "baked" overnight in an oven. This accomplished, any stray grains of sand are removed by an air blower, and the parts reassembled in the "flask." This latter is securely clamped, and the lady is ready to have her complexion cast in bronze.

At this juncture it may be of interest to know that the so-called "sand" used in cores is no plebeian article. It is most decidedly French, and to a crystal hails from the little

FIG. 19   FIG. 20

Preparation of moulds in which one of the leaves of the exterior doors for the Boston Public Library was cast (left), and (right) finished small moulds with corresponding halves left and right. When fitted together, preparatory to pouring the molten bronze, about ¼ to ⅜ of an inch air space existed throughout between upper and lower parts

over this core a wax coating is added to which is imparted the modeling of the original model. A "secret" mixture (used by Cellini among others) about the consistency of cream is then applied carefully over the wax, composed of 50 per cent plaster of Paris (for tenacity), and the balance of brick dust in combination with dry clay, pounded-up crucibles, etc., the latter being unaffected by heat. When one coat has hardened and has filled up all the crevices of the wax, another is given, and so on until a fairly strong coat is built up. Around this are added packed strata of coarse sand, reinforced by rods and metal bands so that the ensemble will withstand the weight of the metal when poured. When all is in readiness it is carefully dried out and baked. The wax naturally melts, leaving a space to be filled by the molten bronze. The cream-coat of plaster of Paris took up all the modeling of the wax, so that the metal on hardening is a replica of the wax relief. The process is widely used for small pilaster capitals, bars as in the marginal diagram, etc. It is evident that if for each groove three cores *A*, *B* and *C* had to be made, more labor would be necessary than with the *cire perdue* preparation. The architect should appreciate the fact that undercutting entails much additional labor, and while the results look the better for it, the costs are naturally higher. If there are to be undercut surfaces or ornament, these should show clearly in the working draw-

ings on which estimates are based. It is unfair to demand extra labor for this refinement of ornament if the extent to which it is wanted is not clearly shown on large-sized details.

After the moulds are completed and are ready to be "poured," the exciting part of the show is in order. Crucibles made of graphite, with an average capacity of about 150 pounds of metal (although there are Goliaths which hold 700 and 900 pounds), contain the metal ingots which have been heated until they are thoroughly fused. At a temperature of about 1700 degrees Fahrenheit the metal is theoretically ready to be poured, but practically it is judged to be "right" by the foundry foreman chiefly by its color. If too red it is too cool, and if white too "thin" or "fluid." If only small moulds are to be poured the crucible is lifted by hand from the furnace, as in Figure 22, while if larger crucibles are employed, mechanical help is resorted to as in Figure 21. Assuming that a small mould is to be poured, say about the size shown in Figure 20, two men are able to do the operation under the eye of the foreman, as in Figure 23. The workman (or "moulder") who made the mould is usually the one to engineer the actual pouring of the molten metal into the form. In Figure 23, he is the one on the right in the photograph, grasping the two handles, while his helper at the other end acts as a pivot man. Having two handles the moulder can direct the actual aim of the spout so that the metal unerringly hits the relatively small funnel which opens into the feeding channels of the mould. The foreman's job is to see that the metal being poured is the right fluidity, and with a bent bar to prevent the dross, which floats on the top of the molten bronze, from flowing into the mould. The excitement comes at this point, with bronze flowing like water and giving off all the colors of the spectrum. It is a good show, with silent actors knowing their cues perfectly. When the metal has filled all possible spaces of the mould, the surplus metal rises in the "vents" or "risers" and comes pouring out to produce a show of splashing gold. It signifies the end of the pouring for that particular form, and the trio of workmen pass on to the next mould.

When a mould requires less than one crucible of metal to satisfy its appetite, the job is a three-man affair as described. But in the case of an equestrian statue or a coffin (as a cheerful example), the preparation is slightly altered, although the same in principle. Figure 24 illustrates a cross-section through a large coffin about 8 feet long, 2 feet 4 inches wide, and 2 feet deep, ready to be poured. Directly above the mould there is erected a basin lined with moulding-sand. At the bottom there are three feeding channels leading to all parts of the mould, and at its mouth (at the bottom of the basin) a sand plug formed around a metal rod with one end extending above the top of the basin. Sufficient molten metal is then poured into the basin so that when the sand plug is

pulled out, the fluid bronze will flood all parts of the mould almost simultaneously. Here the metal thickness would probably be from ¼ to ⅜ of an inch.

When the molten bronze has flooded a mould it takes but a few moments to set and harden. A small grille, the size of the moulds shown in Figure 20, would be ready for cleaning within ten minutes after the time of pouring. This is because the metal is only ⅛ to ¼ of an inch in thickness. Perhaps the statement should be made conversely: the metal must be relatively thin in order that it harden almost immediately. If the metal were poured to form a solid mass or even to be of heavy thickness, it would cool slowly and cause strains and shrinkages; these would disturb the surface so that the finished product would not be a facsimile of the original model. To have the metal heavier than a good pouring thickness adds but little actually to its strength or durability, and thus becomes a liability because of the undesirable shrinkage. The modern tendency is to use an excess of metal, whereas in the classic equestrian statue of Marcus Aurelius the bronze is not only uniformly heavy throughout but is only slightly over ⅛-inch thick, according to Henry Havard in *Les Bronzes d'Art*. It is his opinion that the technical excellence of Roman craftsmen, in their ability to cast bronze relatively thin but of constant thickness, has never since been equalled.

After being poured and cooled the bronze

FIG. 21   FIG. 22

Crucibles of molten bronze being lifted from the oil-burning furnaces—by hand if they are small and with the use of crane if large. The furnaces are below the floor level and out of sight along the wall to the left in both illustrations

is ready for the cleaning and finishing process. First the flask is opened and as much clinging sand is knocked from the bronze casting as is possible. The sand has been burned to a terra-cotta crispness, and that which will not break off is harassed with wire brushes. The inside core is induced to part from the bronze by digging, soaking in water, and further digging. When the casting is freed from sand it is usually a queer-looking octopus, having all manner of extraneous antennæ which were gates and risers before being poured with metal; these are cut off and remelted for the next day's pouring. The casting, thus shorn of all unnecessary appendages, and, having been subjected to vigorous brushing, loses its variegated heat discoloration by being dipped for a moment or two into an acid bath. It comes out with a healthy, reddish glow before the acid has had a chance to etch the surface, and is next plunged into hot water for final riddance of all adhering matter, sand, acid, etc.

The most expensive factor in the production of first-class bronze is the amount of "chasing" (Figure 25), a term glibly used in specifications without a thorough understanding of what it entails and what is specifically wanted. Actually the term signifies the hand labor necessary in removing all small excrescences and "fins" by saws, files, etc., and sharpening and cleaning up every bit of ornament with small chisels, mats, tracers, rifflers, files and the like. Used loosely, it may mean anything from saw-

ing off the main lumps of clinging metal to transforming the piece of work into jewelry. The amount of chasing which the architect desires should be clearly understood by himself and the contractors, not only as far as possible by the wording of his specification, but by a proviso that it shall be done equal to a sample on view at the architect's office. If there be not some definite understanding as to the amount of chasing desired, the identical design might cost anywhere from $1,000 to $5,000, even if estimated and executed by the same foundry. There are cases on record where the architect has so preferred the variations in color of the castings as they came from the moulds that he made a special point about not having any additional work done on them after fins were removed; other architects will not only want a great deal of chasing, but maintain that to execute a craftsmanlike job, the tool marks should be in evidence. That is purely a question of personal taste, but in all cases the estimator of the foundry should know exactly what is expected.

Subsequent to the chasing and filing comes the fitting together of various portions, as would be the case for a counter-screen. When parts are to be fused it is termed "brazing" (Figure 26); this is accomplished by applying a blow-torch until the metal becomes sufficiently hot to melt and fuse together at the juncture, with the aid of a special alloy acting as solder. Sections may of course be joined by being

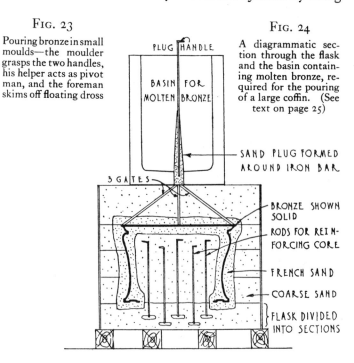

FIG. 23

Pouring bronze in small moulds—the moulder grasps the two handles, his helper acts as pivot man, and the foreman skims off floating dross

FIG. 24

A diagrammatic section through the flask and the basin containing molten bronze, required for the pouring of a large coffin. (See text on page 25)

PLUG HANDLE

BASIN FOR MOLTEN BRONZE

3 GATES

SAND PLUG FORMED AROUND IRON BAR

BRONZE SHOWN SOLID

RODS FOR REINFORCING CORE

FRENCH SAND

COARSE SAND

FLASK DIVIDED INTO SECTIONS

FIG. 25

"Chasing" bronze ornament—refining it with small chisels, files, rifflers, etc. This comprises the most expensive operation

FIG. 26

"Brazing" bronze castings—making separate parts fuse with the aid of special solder and blow torch

screwed or bolted together, but when possible this should always be done so that no screw or bolt-heads are visible on the outside. In exceptional cases they may be necessary, but if the details are drawn with the help of a bronze artisan some solution can usually be found so as not to disfigure exposed faces. Necessary screw heads may often be cajoled into rosettes to good advantage.

Following the fitting are the final steps of polishing, buffing and coloring. Various surfaces and finishes can be obtained and a full range should be submitted to the architect for his selection. There is considerable latitude in both of these, but none as to the *natural* color of the metal. Actual bronze is never anything but the bright and shiny color of a new penny before being handled. If the architect wants anything else he must be sure to specify it, for the rich nut-brown color usually attributed to bronze is acquired by atmospheric oxidation only after long exposure and accompanied by proper care in cleaning. In front of the Pennsylvania Museum in Fairmount Park, Philadelphia, reposes a "Spanish Cannon from Cuba, 1743" (according to the tablet), which has taken on an unbelievable range of colors. There are salmon pinks, pale cadmium oranges, an entire palette of browns, and a long range of greens, from pale emerald to almost veridian. The bronzes in the National Museum of Naples from the excavations of Pompeii are the most rich and varied assortment of greens outside the vegetable kingdom. Almost any color may be obtained by various oxidizing agents, but the change in hue is due to the chemical action which takes place on the *surface only*. Chloride of ammonia, as well as common salt and vinegar, will react to produce beautiful greens, while various browns can be coaxed with the application of sulphide of potassium. It is im-

portant that the craftsman's instructions to the client concerning the care of the bronze should be meticulously followed, because a moron of a cleaner or janitor can ruin the best "patina" in about two minutes.

Treating the surface of bronze in one way or another to give a desired color affects the surface only, and on scratching the surface with any sharp point the bright metal will shine through. There is no action here comparable to rust on iron, which eats away the material. Oxidation or weathering will affect bronze to perhaps a millimeter in depth and will not only go no further, but actually forms a coating which prevents further inroads of atmospheric aggression, thus accounting for the attribute of bronze's being the "eternal metal."

It might be mentioned in passing that rolled, drawn, and "extruded bronze" is not generally the same as cast bronze in color, and is bound to appear differently after exposure. If *finesse* and color are more important to the architect than cost, he should not use cast bronze with the others because of the difficulty in matching colors, the promises of contractors notwithstanding (Extruded Bronze, page 33). On an over-hurried Fifth Avenue shop-front the pilasters were made of "extruded bronze" and the cast ornament on them screwed in place later, the idea being that the store could not open without pilasters. At the time it seemed a feasible scheme, but as it worked out it would have been better practice if cast iron frames and supports for the show-window glass had first been erected and painted for the store's opening, and the cast bronze pilasters applied later. The client would have paid no more, the bronze man could have done a creditable job, and the architect would have been proud of the result.

THE CARE OF BRONZE

AN architect may design beautiful bronze doors and the bronze contractor cast them perfectly, yet within five years they may not be a credit to either, because of inadequate or improper care on the part of the client. It is an old problem, of course, successfully to impress on clients that theirs is a responsibility which neither architect nor contractor can assume after the completion of the building. If bronze is to serve its purpose of beautifying an edifice it must be cared for regularly in an intelligent manner. No client thinks it an extravagance to place a regular contract for window-cleaning, yet he will not cheerfully consider a similar agreement for the weekly care of his exterior bronze unless its necessity is duly stressed by the architect. One of the outstanding banks of New York City has a beautiful bronze window with ornamental frame and engaged columns above the main entrance; the glass is religiously cleaned regularly, yet the bronze has not been touched since it was erected. After the next hard coal strike there may not appear to be any ornament whatsoever. Flat *rinceau* ornament 20 feet above the pavement is not worth doing in bronze if it is not to be properly cared for, and amounts to so much useless investment on the part of the owner. All the conscientious efforts of the architect, modeler and artisan to create a thing of beauty are almost valueless as the bronze continues to become blacker and sootier. It is true of course that the famous Ghiberti doors of the Florence Baptistry (pages 52-57) have not been cleaned once a week, but at present there are not many modern examples where the ornament is almost freestanding as on those, and therefore cannot be smothered by dirt; nor, again, have we many cities as free from soot as Florence.

When the architect is discussing materials with his client at the outset, he should not make the assertion that bronze requires no care such as other metals—wrought or cast iron, for examples. It is only fair to the client that he be told that bronze should be cleaned regularly. Exterior work should be wiped off about once a week with a dry cloth, followed by another moistened with crude, lemon or linseed oil, or wax, to clean it and prevent excessive oxidation. Where bronze has long been left uncared for and it is desired to restore a rich brown color, some bronze contractor should be given the job of applying some "sharp water" (dilute acid) and reconditioning the finish. Unintelligent cleaning of bronze usually results in shiny high-lights on the highest relief of the ornament and a sordid range of green and black polish-débris in all depressions. More variety than though it were cast iron instead of bronze, to be sure, but scarcely more beautiful!

A not uncommon modern practice is to have the bronze contractor apply lacquer to interior work in the hope that it will continue to remain in the same state as when it leaves the foundry's finishing department. It is questionable whether this is sound practice, because sooner or later the lacquer will wear off certain areas. What follows is that the bare spots oxidize because of exposure to the air and very soon they begin to appear quite different in color from the areas still covered by lacquer. Almost every one can recollect seeing bronze doors in lamentable condition, because of the lacquer coating wearing off, leaving ugly, irregular splotches to disfigure the finish. The expense of removing all the lacquer, in the attempt to give the surface a uniform appearance anew, will cost more than proper *regular* care from the day of installation.

SOME PRACTICAL ASPECTS

WHEN the architect is discussing time requirements for the various materials, he may have difficulty in approximating the period necessary for the completion of the bronze work. Even the bronze contractor may be unable to determine this exactly, because of not knowing how long certain work not under his control will require. Some kinds of bronze work might

be furnished within a month, but it would be exceptional cast bronze which could be delivered on the job so soon after signing the contract. Six to eight weeks would be a better minimum to count upon, while a complicated problem, such as a richly ornamented counter-screen, would be more apt to take from three to four months. Following is a list of the operations and steps figuring in the time element, in the order they occur from the date when the bronze contractor has been authorized to proceed after his estimate has been accepted:

(1) Details received from the architect's office, working drawings prepared and sent back for checking. (Two weeks under favorable circumstances; more likely three or four.)

(2) Mill material ordered when shop drawings were being checked, but shipments may be slow and hold up work. (Assume material arrives on time.)

(3) Accurate measurements obtained from job or general contractor. (This can be done while the working drawings are being made and checked.)

(4) Models received from the sculptor or modeler, and patterns begun. (Three or four additional weeks at least; total, so far, about five weeks.)

(5) Wood or metal patterns to be made. (Two weeks; total, about seven weeks.)

(6) Making moulds and pouring castings. (Two weeks; total, about nine weeks.)

(7) Filing, fitting, and chasing. (Two weeks; total, about eleven weeks.)

(8) Grinding, polishing, coloring. (One week; total, about twelve weeks.)

(9) Delivery and erection. (Two weeks; total, about fourteen weeks.)

The above list is only an approximation, of course, for a strike or labor dispute in Timbuctoo may tie a bronze contractor's hands. He may have extraordinarily good luck, on the other hand, and sail along in better time. The list, however, gives the architect some idea of what delays the bronze contractor is subject to, and he can understand that, unless his scale- and full-size drawings are forthcoming at once after contracts are awarded, nothing can be started. Also, unless shop drawings are promptly checked they will hold up the entire procedure. Any help the architect can give the modeler, by criticising models when they are ready instead of procrastinating, will expedite the work and see it finished with much better workmanship than if he delays. Too often he puts the contractor days behind schedule, and then attempts to "speed things up" by jumping on the blameless fellow at the time when the job would have been complete had the architect shown the speed in his own work which he expects of the foundry in theirs.

It is human nature to pity oneself for having the toughest row to hoe, and the architect usually decides, without ever going near a bronze foundry, that no contractor has as many worries or as meagre financial return as he. But, as stated previously, bronze men seem a good-natured sort and allow architects to believe themselves martyrs without raising a peep in protest. However, it is probably infinitely more difficult to run a foundry than a drafting-room. There are many more complicating circumstances, certainly. Except in rare cases of specialists, architectural draftsmen can be replaced without great difficulty; they do not have unions; being brought up on the *charrette* idea, they do not have religious notions about stopping work with the whistle, organizing "walk-outs," or quitting in sympathy because of a confrère's being "fired"; no foreman dictates to the architect who shall and who shall not work on various jobs. The increase in price of thumb-tacks and tracing-paper will not wipe out an architect's profit overnight and make him continue to work on for months, knowing that each day his losses are piling up. Compared with the foundry chief the architect little realizes what a carefree existence his is! A drawing can always be lettered: "Continue ornament," or "Details to be furnished to contractor later," or "Contractor to work out this condition on job." But the contractor must cast all of his ornament, must deliver all details when they are called for, and must work out all the hard corners which the architect's draftsmen could not or did not care to delve into.

On the other hand, there is something to be said for the architect who conscientiously does all that can be expected toward expediting details, approving models promptly, and who is, above all, anxious that his client be given the product that he is paying for. Some foundries are wont to give excellent service to the large offices which keep them supplied with work, but consider the small architect as legitimate prey on which to make up for their losses on other jobs. An actual order sent by the head of one of the largest bronze men to his shop foreman, written in his own handwriting and signed, was as follows: "Use cheapest construction possible, disregard architect's details. You must save $12,000; that is, reduce the cost that much by simplifying all items." In all fairness to his clients the architect should be sufficiently well informed on the subject of good bronze work so that he will insist on the rejection of all work not fulfilling the specifications, and when the contractor has obviously pursued a policy as the above quotation outlines, future bids from such a company should be refused. It would be doing both the architectural profession and the bronze industry a favor if dishonest and poor workmanship were made public and the foundry responsible were refused further work. If there be a wide discrepancy between estimates, when the architect's drawings and specifications are definite, the architect will automatically have to be on his guard and may well post a representative at the foundry to watch work from the time it comes from the sand until it is erected; either he may find his reputation ruined by disgracefully executed work, or otherwise he must persuade the owner to wait several months for the building to open while new bronze is cast. If the foundry is being paid one hundred cents on the dollar for first-class bronze, there is no reason why the architect should not demand one hundred per cent workmanship. Too often the architect never sees the bronze work until it is being erected on the job and then, although the flaws are frightful, he cannot afford to reject it because of an "opening date," when the work must be completed. It might not have happened had he sent a representative to the foundry after the castings were made, at a time when there was still an opportunity for recasting them. Some offices are so slightly acquainted with what good bronze work should be that they accept disreputable work as a matter of course. Ignorance of that sort cannot be condoned with plentiful old and new work on record, eloquently representing what bronze should achieve. Shoddy work does as much harm to the bronze trade as to the architectural profession.

The designer has less to cramp him in cast bronze than in almost any other metal, that is, he can use almost any sort of ornament and not trespass in a field more characteristic of another material. In wrought iron, *e. g.*, there are definite traits which, if violated, not only make the design look faulty but compel the craftsman to execute a *tour-de-force*. In bronze almost everything is in character except the twisted bar. This is really a possession of a wrought material, for if a plain twist is to be executed in bronze it must be treated as wrought work and twisted (when cold), or if there were to be ornamentation on the bar in

addition to the twist, the "lost-wax" process might be employed. The most minute detail can be obtained in bronze because the sand of the mould will take up practically all the surfacing that the model has to offer, be the lines ever so slight. Also, for pierced work bronze will suffer itself to be more emaciated than any other cast building metal. When a cast iron member is diminished to $\frac{1}{4}$ of an inch in width, it has just about reached the minimum, while bronze can be diminished a fraction more.

Architects having draftsmen employed on full-size details for bronze work would probably save themselves time by carefully going over the drawings before they are sent to the modeler. Unless a man has previously done bronze detailing, his initial attempts are almost sure to be of wood, terra-cotta or stone character, and not nearly fine enough in scale. Not only is this poor design, but, because of additional metal, needlessly adds to the expense. Such firms as McKim, Mead & White, and York & Sawyer, usually have the modeler paint the plaster model a bronze color before final approval. Detail which on white plaster appears to be in correct relief, may be entirely too flat when cast in bronze. Since a certain amount of crispness is lost through casting, the models should be made a trifle sharper in detail than is desired in the finished bronze.

In the small but valuable book by Henry Harvard, *Les Bronzes d'Art*, referred to earlier, the point is well taken that many a modern sculptor or modeler designs in plastic clay without realizing the importance of knowing whether it is to be executed in the dense bronze, capable of minute scale, or in a coarser material, such as marble or stone. Any student of ancient or Renaissance bronzes appreciates what deliberation must have gone into their modeling, for the results bespeak a complete mastery of interpretation in a material susceptible to a high degree of surfacing and *finesse* of detail.

It is no sin for the architect to be unfamiliar with how bronze work is best detailed and constructed, yet most bronze artisans find that the architect is not only loath to confess his ignorance, but refuses the aid to which he would be welcome. In the presence of client or drafting force the architectural dictator probably feels that it is properly his rôle to "dominate the situation," and in so doing embarrasses and invokes the ill-will of the bronze man. Before the architect has seen bronze develop from blue-prints through the erection stage and knows whereof he speaks, it is decidedly to his advantage to learn all he possibly can from an accommodating and intelligent artisan.

Consultation with a foundry man, when the working drawings are in progress, is advantageous to the architect in more ways than one. Incomplete understanding of bronze may easily cause the estimates to exceed the client's allowance, whereas an equally good or better effect might have been attained by careful consideration of details in collaboration with a specialist. It would take a little of the architect's time, but it would be well worth it. Viewed coldly and commercially, more knowledge means more money. It is not profitable for an architect to first design bronze, receive estimates which are too high, and have to be satisfied with some substitute as a last resort. Such a proceeding costs the architect additional drafting expenses, loss in consultation time, and disappointment that the bronze was not executed as first shown on the studies and working drawings. When a bronze estimate exceeds the allowance, the architect may try to economize on ornament in an attempt to come within the budget limit, but after impoverishing the ornament here and there he may be chagrined to discover that a new estimate is not appreciably lower then the first. Consequently he sometimes draws the incorrect conclusion that bronze is too rich for *his* clients' purses and decides that he has learned his lesson. He might be surprised if some bronze expert were to demonstrate at the foundry that some of the ornament which he deleted, serving only to impoverish the appearance of the design, actually made more work for the foundry by its absence. Ridiculous as that may sound, it is true in the case of a cast door, let us say, with three panels vertically: to eliminate the ornament from the upper two and substitute plain panels does not mean less work, for whereas the ornament would have broken up the surface so that any minute imperfections in the casting would not show, smooth areas would require infinite pains in polishing to get a perfect finish. Such would not be the case for a built-up door of extruded sections or sheet panels, of course, but for a cast one it would. It is unfair to one's self to make decisions for or against any material without full knowledge concerning it, and, for the sake of the architect's own reputation, it is well worth his time to consult with a bronze man in designing and

detailing, at least until his experience has taught what is and what is not good economic shop practice.

One of the greatest problems of the bronze contractor is to be able to make an intelligent estimate from the architect's drawings. If the architect has details at $\frac{3}{4}$-inch scale, with an occasional full-size detail, and a specification which is absolutely definite, the estimator can give an accurate price which will be fair to his company as well as to the client. It will be a square competition between the bidders, and gives fair assurance that there will be no cause for extras, hard feelings, pitched battles, or loss to the foundry. On the other hand, if working drawing details be only at $\frac{1}{8}$- or $\frac{1}{4}$-inch scale, the estimator has two alternatives: he may take into account that the architect will expect more elaborate workmanship than what is barely indicated on the drawings, and therefore add a generous percentage for the unknown requirements existent only in the architect's mind, thus submitting a higher bid than necessary if the protection of the foundry were not at stake; the second option is to take a chance by figuring only on what is shown, resulting in an estimate insufficient to cover any later elaboration of full-size details by the architect, and which will cause a loss unless an "extra" be granted.

The average race-track "bookie" hardly knows what chance-taking is compared to the lot of the bronze estimator, for to interpret literally the vast majority of plans and specifications, would mean either never getting any work in the foundry or taking jobs which resulted only in losses. An architect may voluntarily chance a few hundred dollars with a set of sketches now and then, but never is he driven to the sheer gambling into which he forces the bronze companies. When great divergence in bronze estimates exists, the foundry submitting the highest bid should not be condemned as being "too high priced," because cost variations are often due to one company's taking less of a chance than another. If only high-class foundries bid, the differences are apt to represent what the estimators think the architect will later require but which he does not specify, and the greater the range of estimates, the more certain that the plans and specifications are ambiguous (refer to page 189).

If the architect would attempt to take off the quantities for an estimate from his own drawings he would realize the importance of clarity. Ornament particularly should be accurately lettered, on ¾- or 1-inch scale details, as to whether it is single or double faced, to what extent it is repeated, what models will be supplied by the modeler (enclosed by dotted lines on the working drawings) so that the foundry man knows how much additional work he must do before proceeding with moulds, etc. There should be added any further information which will make absolutely definite the exact character of the work. Parts to be extruded should be clearly marked as such, and similarly for portions cast. The nature of all ornament should be so shown that there is no occasion for the slightest doubt; undercutting cannot later be expected unless clearly noted on the contract plans. The ideal condition would be to issue enough full-size details for estimate, so that the exact nature of all types of ornament would be shown in profile and a small portion in elevation, for that would mean an accurate estimate, as fair to the foundry as to the client. A bid so low that the contractor losses money does the architect no good, because there will naturally be an attempt to skimp to reduce losses, and the final outcome is unlikely to represent first-class workmanship. There will also be unpleasant memories of verbal and literary combats which ensued in the contractor's bombardment for an "extra," and in the client's failure to understand why the artisan should apparently have good cause for complaint against the architect.

If a first-class bronze company is doing the work, an architect will be able to save both time and drafting expense. After the awarding of the contract there should be a conference and an understanding of what is necessary for the architect to draw out. Generally the construction which goes on behind the ornamented faces is beyond the architect's knowledge, and what he does draw is of little or no use to the bronze draftsmen. Special conditions and suggestions should be discussed with a representative of the foundry, but, for the most part, if profiles are given and sufficient ornamentation shown in elevation, particularly at intersections, corners, exceptional places, etc., there will be no necessity for laboriously working out mechanical devices or constructional connections.

One of the chief difficulties of the bronze contractor is that his work is held up by a number of factors. First is the architect, who is likely not only to be slow in issuing the full-size details, but also is apt to work out the most elaborate conditions last without realizing that these are the parts which will take the greatest time to cast and complete. Even after the architect's drawings are received, the foundry may still be retarded by failure to obtain dimensions dependent upon revolving doors, elevator shafts for the cabs and doors, marble openings for grilles, or distances between columns or piers for counter-screens, and so on without limitation. When the bronze is delivered at the building it must fit exactly, so until all the governing over-all dimensions are received from other trades, a great portion of the foundry work cannot even be started. Unfortunately also, the bronze work is the last put in place and any and all delays which have caused its tardiness are forgotten, all blame for the late completion of the building being dumped at the door of the guiltless foundry.

Although too much help cannot be accepted before the drawings are out for estimate, the architect does well to guard against revisions by the low bidder after the estimate has been approved, assuming the best possible manner of detailing and specifying has been pursued with the aid of expert advice. If the low bidder has suggestions to make they should in all fairness be considered, but with an eye alert to detect changes which will cheapen the job and not improve it. Before accepting alterations, if he be uncertain, the architect should obtain disinterested counsel. Particularly emphatic should the architect be in having the contractor understand that under no conditions are suggestions to be taken to the client directly, and the idea "sold" to the latter that it is perfectly good and perhaps a little better to use cheap sheets and assembled stock sections in place of the material as shown on the drawings. Sometimes the client can be made to waver by the "tremendous saving" which the contractor can effect, and if the architect is to permit his responsibility to pass out of his hands, it is losing his standing as the client's representative first, and, because of poor resultant work, his reputation second. Certain foundries have a habit of so doing, and in protecting the pursuit of architecture as a profession, the only recourse is concertedly to join in prohibiting such offending companies from even submitting an estimate.

EXTRUDED BRONZE

THE term "extruded bronze" and the product have become so widely used that the average architect may have come to think that in using it he is getting a form of bronze which is simply cheaper than the cast article. As a matter of actual chemical analysis, it is not bronze at all, but brass containing lead; it is heated in billets to a cherry red and forced by hydraulic pressure through a steel die in almost any profile imaginable. The content of extruded brass (more properly so termed from the alloy make-up) usually consists of from 54 to 57 per cent copper, 2 to 2½ per cent lead and the remainder zinc. When the bronze foundries agree to match their cast work in color with extruded, they often find it more difficult to do than to promise; when they do succeed it is because the alloy used in the casting coincides with the extruded product, omitting the 7 per cent or more of tin usual in bronze.

It is only fair to "extruded bronze," and to the architect and client as well, that the physical properties of the material be recognized and realized. Since the alloy is not bronze it cannot be expected to weather like bronze, and if it tarnishes like old cast brass automobile trimmings or plumbing fittings, the reason is evident. The work may be expertly lacquered by a spraying device, and for exterior exposure such finish may last for two years, but if at the end of that time, or even before, the finish becomes a swarthy black either in spots or all over, the architect's reputation ought not to suffer because he thought he was getting something "just as good" as cast bronze. It may be said in behalf of extruded sections that their exterior corners are sharper than could be obtained in cast work, that lines are apt to be perfectly true and without flaws, and that for certain work which must necessarily be erected economically, the product serves a useful purpose. Certainly it is apt to be superior to cast iron or copper for shop fronts with small-scale pilasters and like architectural features. It should *never* be used for column shafts, because there is no entasis possible, but if extruded work be necessary to come within a budget allowance, in place of columns there should be designed square piers, engaged piers or pilasters. The practice of building up pilasters, panels, entablatures, etc., of stock profiles, fitting them together and planting ornament on them like so many wood members, may serve its purpose, just as a Ford car may fulfill certain missions as well as a Lincoln automobile. The makers of "extruded bronze" do not pretend it is cast bronze, and neither should the bronze foundries or the architect. The client should have a right to know what it is he is paying for and what he may expect. If he is satisfied with a Ford chassis, body and top, embellished by Lincoln upholstery and radiator cap, all well and good.

The designer has certain limitations in designing work which is to be extruded. The steel die through which the heated billet is forced is 8 inches in diameter, consequently any profile which he wants to have in a single piece must fit within a circle 6 inches in diameter, 1 inch all around the outside being necessary for the strength of the die. Also, in solid sections where there are grooves these cannot be greater in depth than their width, or the strength of the die will be too weakened. Profiles which transgress both of these limitations of the die can be overcome if the section can be extruded in more than one member. An advantage in extruded sections is that for many members it is possible to form dove-tailed profiles which make an excellent fitting. Plain facias are not affected by the above die limitations, since they can be made up of sheets which come in 48-inch widths. These may be anything in thickness from 2 inches down. Tubing is much employed in door sections and varies from 12 to 18 gauge. The content for sheets and tubing is generally 85 parts of copper to 15 of zinc, while if used with extruded members (in order to match the color of cast bronze), the copper is reduced to 60 and the zinc increased to 40 per cent.

Extruded brass does not tarnish with the same rapidity as cast brass, probably because its density in being forced through the die is less porous than would be the case in a casting. One of the problems attendant upon extrusion is that as the metal comes from the die it writhes in a trough, and on cooling must be straightened by hand hammering after it has cooled. Unless this is most carefully done the edges and surfaces will be warped and untrue. After erection it would seem that the best method for caring for it would be to have it naturally finished *without* lacquer, and to stress the necessity of employing only intelligent help to clean it regularly with a dry cloth moistened with oil, the same as for cast bronze (page 28).

FIG. 27.—BRONZE DOORS, SANCTUARY S. MICHELE, MONTE S. ANGELO. (1076)
The general scheme of both doors and stone setting are particularly applicable to
modern practice because of their simplicity of design and low cost of execution

FIG. 28.—DETAIL OF BRONZE DOORS, BASILICA OF ST. MARK'S, VENICE

While the identical ornament may not be desirable in a modern building, the relative
inexpensiveness of this *type* of ornament should lead to popular emulation and usage

FIG. 29.—BRONZE DOORS TO TOMB OF BOEMUND, CANOSA DI PUGLIA. (1115)
This varied yet simple vocabulary, consisting of ornament in low relief and niello with occasional accents in high relief, might
advantageously be translated into modern parlance, making due allowance for alterations which seem to have taken place

FIG. 30.—REPOUSSÉ BRONZE DOORS, S. ZENO MAGGIORE, VERONA. (1171)

Perhaps the most applicable feature for modern design is that of the pierced stile and rail members, which suggest an invigorating departure from the usual mouldings or flat straps. All of the ornamentation has been beaten out and applied to the wood doors, indicating that the metal may more properly be termed brass than bronze. There is a definite metallic quality present throughout, achieved by naïve simplicity. The episodes depicted start at the top and read down, the right half dealing with Old Testament history, and the left half with the New. The panels at the centre not enclosed by the regular stile and rail members bear no seeming relation to the remainder of the door, and may very possibly be the result of an alteration to the original composition

FIG. 31.—BRONZE DOORS, CATHEDRAL OF TROJA. (TWELFTH CENTURY)
The unprecedented distribution and variation of color, ranging from freestanding modeling to incised silver lines,
are more than enviable assets; except for the surplus knockers these doors should command great respect in design

FIG. 32.—DETAIL OF BRONZE DOORS, CATHEDRAL OF TROJA. (TWELFTH CENTURY)

Only rarely within so limited an area are there to be found so many versions of bronze ornamentation all in excellent taste, and evidencing as well a knowledge of how the metal can best display itself to advantage

FIG. 33.—BRONZE DOORS, CATHEDRAL OF BENEVENTO. (1150)

Doors strangely Classic with regular panelling and egg-and-dart mouldings are made still more singular by comparison with those of Troja—both being credited to Oderisius of Benevento.   The repeating panels compose a quieting base for the restlessness above
(detail on page opposite)

FIG. 34.—DETAIL OF BRONZE PANELS, CATHEDRAL OF BENEVENTO

There is an admirable contrast in the manner in which the egg-and-dart modeling is in bold relief, while that of the knocker head and the two isolated figures under simplified pediments is flat and simple. The upper right-hand panel might have profited with less relief

(refer to page opposite)

FIG. 35.—BRONZE DOORS, CATHEDRAL OF RAVELLO. (BARISANUS OF TRANI, 1179)

A pleasant variation is present due to the projecting rosettes and two knocker heads, in contrast with the over-all flat modeling, as well as the repeating panels below complementing the diversified ones above

FIG. 36.—DETAIL OF BRONZE DOORS, CATHEDRAL OF RAVELLO. (SEE PAGE OPPOSITE)
The panels are bolted to the wood backing and held by studs or rosettes at the intersections of stiles
and rails in quite the same manner as the older wood doors. The general flatness of the modeling is
entirely in character with the ornamentation of the Cathedral, particularly the mosaics. The doors
exemplify Romanesque bronze at its best, and display characteristic figure and animal ornamentation

FIG. 37.—NORTH BRONZE DOORS, CATHEDRAL OF MONREALE.
(BARISANUS OF TRANI, 1180?)

The design and arrangement of the panels are noteworthy in that each horizontal row presents a repeating characteristic, except in the four corners. The flatness and scale of the ornament is particularly suited to the surrounding mosaics. Sagging panels frankly indicate the manner of forging or casting separate small units and then bolting or nailing them to a wood core

FIG. 38.—WEST BRONZE DOORS, CATHEDRAL OF MONREALE.
(BONANNO DA PISA, 1186)
While there are admirable features about this door, its multiplication of vertical stiles leaves only
relatively small panels and produces a less satisfying result than the North doors (opposite page)

FIG. 39.—BRONZE DOORS OF TRANSEPT, CATHEDRAL OF PISA. (BONANNO DA PISA, 1180)
The unusual arrangement of top and bottom panels running the breadth of each leaf is probably not disturbing because of the richer color in the bottom one, and the accented figure in the centre of the top. A modern door recently followed this panelling scheme without analyzing the panel ornamentation, with unfortunate results

FIG. 40.—DETAIL OF BRONZE PANELS, TRANSEPT DOOR, CATHEDRAL OF PISA
These scenes from the life of Christ—washing the disciples' feet, the Last Supper, being tempted by the devil, the Transfiguration, at the well, and the flight into Egypt—are modeled with dramatic and epic quality of the first water and, at the same time, in a manner which leaves no doubt as to their metallic fabric

FIG. 41.—DETAIL OF MINOR BRONZE DOORS, BASILICA OF ST. MARK'S, VENICE

Although the design *parti* is not very unusual, there are refreshing features in the raised round accents where the "fish-scale" openings join, in the flowers in the openings bordering the horizontal division, and in the rail ornamentation

FIG. 42.—DETAIL OF MAIN BRONZE DOORS, BASILICA OF ST. MARK'S, VENICE

A thirteenth-century version of the "fish-scale" pattern, with accents similar to the earlier door (shown above) where the arches are joined, but with a horizontal division carried out by an unusual repetition of slightly varied lions' heads

FIG. 43.—LEFT BRONZE DOORS, MAIN FAÇADE, CATHEDRAL OF PISA

Although there was more technical skill required in the casting of doors such as these than panels in low relief, they can scarcely be hailed as successful architecturally as those of the earlier Romanesque régime

FIG. 44.—SOUTH BRONZE DOORS OF BAPTISTRY, FLORENCE CATHEDRAL. (C. 1330)

These doors by Andrea Pisano were the prototype for the general *parti* of the later ones by Ghiberti (page 53). They possess a quiet dignity, aided no doubt by the simplified lower rows of panels after the manner of some of the earlier doors

FIG. 45.—BRONZE DOORS TO THE NEW SACRISTRY, CATHEDRAL OF FLORENCE

These doors by Lucca della Robbia, in conjunction with Michelozzo and Maso di Bartolomeo (1446-'67), are noteworthy for the composition of the panels; while all vary, yet each is harmoniously and similarly grouped around a central figure

FIG. 46.—DETAIL OF CENTRE PANELS, LEFT LEAF OF NORTH DOOR OF BAPTISTRY, FLORENCE CATHEDRAL
Lorenzo Ghiberti's masterpiece for all time in architectural bronze is shown in entirety on the page opposite, with details following

FIG. 47.—NORTH BRONZE DOORS OF BAPTISTRY, FLORENCE CATHEDRAL. (1425–'52)
Ghiberti's ability as a sculptor of architectural bronze has never been surpassed; he realized the *finesse* of which the metal was capable and the necessity of refining cast detail. The variety in the modeling and the contrasts of plain and enriched surfaces are above reproach

FIG. 49.—NORTH AND SOUTH DOOR JAMBS, FLORENCE BAPTISTRY
The relative flatness, contrasted with the freestanding ornamentation shown to
the left, evinces a nice understanding and fitting usage by Ghiberti (pages 50 and 53)

FIG. 48.—BRONZE ARCHIVOLT, SOUTH DOOR, FLORENCE BAPTISTRY
A surrounding band of applied bronze ornament was added to the south door—begun
by Lorenzo Ghiberti and completed by Vittorio Ghiberti and others (page 50)

BRONZE: ILLUSTRATIONS

FIG. 50 (ABOVE) AND 51 (BELOW).—DETAILS OF ARCHIVOLT SURROUNDING NORTH AND SOUTH DOORS, FLORENCE BAPTISTRY

Above is shown the archivolt by Lorenzo Ghiberti for the north door (page 53), and below, the one started by him but completed by his followers after his death, for the south door (page 50). Modern employment of bronze in any style can learn valuable lessons from the contrasts brought into play, together with the minute scale and varied surfacing

FIG. 52 (LEFT) AND 53 (RIGHT).—DETAILS OF NORTH DOOR ARCHIVOLT, FLORENCE BAPTISTRY

Without a doubt much of the charm of these bronze details lies in the absence of hackneyed repetition of forms; animals are expertly modeled and foliage is represented by leaves and flowers of many species (page 53)

FIG. 54 (LEFT) AND 55 (RIGHT).—EAST AND SOUTH DOOR ARCHIVOLTS, FLORENCE BAPTISTRY
The left detail is by Lorenzo Ghiberti, while the other was begun by him but completed after his death; both
would cause financial despair to the modern foundryman because of the undercutting of ornament (page 50)

FIG. 56.—CENTRE BRONZE DOORS, ST. PETER'S, ROME.   (1439 OR 1445 ?)
The large-scaled architectural setting makes these doors (executed by Filarete assisted by
Simone) appear suitable, but otherwise they would likely seem ponderous in scale for bronze work

FIG. 57.—DETAIL OF LOWER LEFT SECTION, DOORS OF ST. PETER'S, ROME

The well-populated *rinceau* is one of the doors' most successful features, not only for the dexterous manner in which details are incorporated, but for serving as an adequate frame for the large panels

FIG. 58.—MEASURED DRAWING OF BAPTISTRY DOOR, PISTOIA

While the door is of wood its employment of bronze studs is of special interest because of
the important part they play in enriching the design.   (See photographs on page opposite)

FIG. 59 (LEFT) AND 60 (RIGHT).—ENTIRE VIEW AND DETAIL OF BAPTISTRY DOOR, PISTOIA

The entire door, although relieved from monotony by the well-designed and well-executed wood carving, requires the bronze studs to bring the stiles into scale

Whereas in a photograph the wood door and bronze studs appear the same color, in reality there is an engaging difference between staid browns and lively greens

FIG. 61.—BRONZE GRILLE, CHAPEL OF GABRIEL DE ZAPORTA IN THE OLD CATHEDRAL OF SARAGOSSA. (1579)

This *reja* follows the same general *parti* as the usual wrought iron compositions, and, while having but few confrères in bronze, is perfectly suited to the material. All of the Spanish *rejas* executed in iron having this type of moulded spindle and carved arabesque are of course much better suited to a cast than a forged metal

BRONZE: ILLUSTRATIONS

FIG. 62.—BRONZE GRILLE, CHURCH OF THE INCORONATA, LODI. (ITALIAN, 1550)

The composition of this grille is not unusual with its series of moulded spindles, but the introduction between them of cupids' heads with folded wings, is stimulatingly un-sophisticated. The arabesques on the pilasters hold a suggestion for modern work by being sunk instead of raised—a simple achievement for present-day facilities (page 188)

BRONZE GRILLE IN THE CAPELLA DEL
SACRO CINGOLO (CHAPEL OF THE SACRED
GIRDLE), CATHEDRAL OF PRATO

FIG. 63 (above), a general view of the chapel showing the location of its fifteenth-century bronze work
FIG. 64 (right), a detail of the repeating circular
motif, and the vertical *rinceau* forming the end panels
FIG. 65 (below), a detail of the pierced frieze and
the bases of the cresting units and candlesticks

Since bronze has been used so rarely in grilles, it is
all the more inspirational that one so exquisite in detail and satisfying in composition should, as it were,
suddenly have sprung into being from Vulcan's brain

FIG. 66 (LEFT) AND 67 (RIGHT).—DETAILS OF BRONZE GRILLE, CHAPEL OF THE SACRED GIRDLE, PRATO
Except for the mixture of an adapted Gothic quatrefoil with purely Classic-Renaissance details, the design is without a peer in the realm of bronze grilles.   (Attributed to Simone, and Bruno di Ser Lapo and Pasquino di Matteo [?])

FIG. 69.—BRONZE DETAIL OF SIDE DOOR, CATHEDRAL OF FLORENCE
While one may disagree with the handling of the ornament and desire more discriminating restraint, it shows the innate possibilities of bronze. (By G. Cassioli)

FIG. 68.—BRONZE DETAIL OF MAIN DOOR, CATHEDRAL OF FLORENCE
An illustration of what may be expected and accomplished with bronze—bas-reliefs flat, raised and three-quarters freestanding. (By Prof. A. Passaglia)

BRONZE: ILLUSTRATIONS

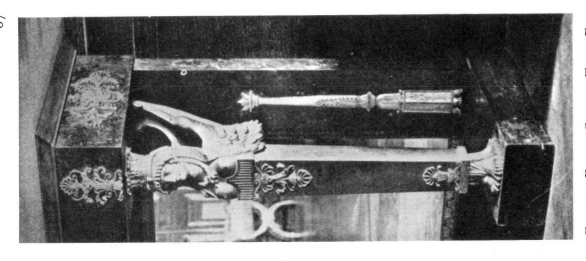

FIG. 72.—EMPIRE CONSOLE TABLE END

A restrained and intelligent version of a caryatid at Fontainebleau, executed in bronze and ebony

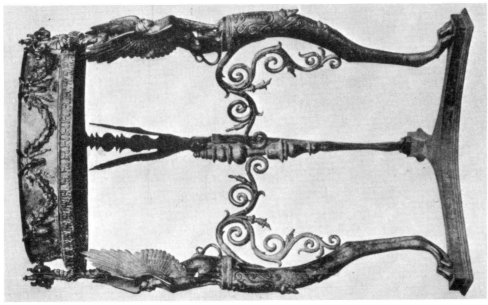

FIG. 71.—GRECO-ROMAN TABLE OF BRONZE

This table is obviously of metal because of the lightness of its legs, the wings, and the scroll brackets, and also, the fine scale of its ornament. Modern bronze errs almost always in the excessive heaviness of parts, giving the impression that a wood or stone design has been merely relabelled to be executed in metal. Unless the designer and the craftsman are alive to the inherent characteristics of the material it is only natural that the results should be pathetically inferior to the many prototypes which could successfully be followed

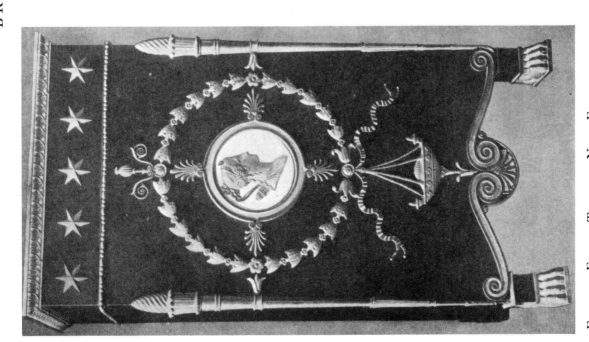

FIG. 70.—EMPIRE TABLE DE NUIT, FONTAINEBLEAU

The success of boldly combining bronze with a black background is produced only by thoughtful study and a keen sense of propriety

METAL CRAFTS IN ARCHITECTURE

Fig. 73.—Bronze Table Centre-Piece of Charles X
Nineteenth-century French bronzes achieved a *finesse* of modeling and surfacing which was equal to anything previous, and, more than that, was quite appropriate to the metal

Fig. 74.—French Bronze Urn in the Greek Manner
Another illustration showing the ability of the nineteenth-century French craftsmen who grasped the lessons of the ancients

BRONZE: ILLUSTRATIONS

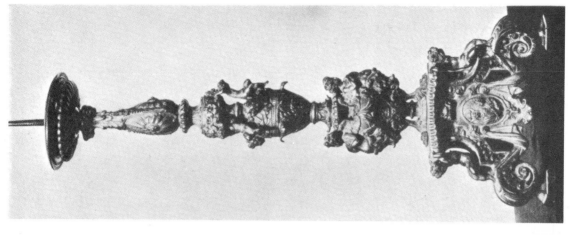

FIG. 77.—CANDELABRA, BOLOGNA
This bronze by Giovanni da Bologna was
executed in an age undaunted by undercuts

FIG. 76.—FOOT OF GILDED BRONZE CROSS, ITALIAN (1541)
In contrast with Leopardi's flagpole base this bronze is 10 inches at its greatest base dimension. On two of the faces are enamelled silver medallions

FIG. 75.—FLAGPOLE BASE, ST. MARK'S
Alessandro Leopardi's ornament is varied in
relief, and weighted with civic symbolism

FIG. 78.—BRONZE DOORS, KNICKERBOCKER TRUST COMPANY, NEW YORK CITY

McKim, Mead & White, Architects   Jno. Williams, Inc., Craftsmen

FIG. 79.—BRONZE DOORS, FAIRHAVEN MEMORIAL CHURCH, FAIRHAVEN, MASSACHUSETTS
Charles Brigham, Architect   Jno. Williams, Inc., Craftsmen

FIG. 80.—BRONZE ELEVATOR DOORS, BOWERY SAVINGS BANK, NEW YORK CITY
York & Sawyer, Architects   Wm. H. Jackson Company, Craftsmen
(Each pair approximately 4 by 7 feet)

FIG. 81.—BRONZE DOORS OF MAIN ENTRANCE, BOWERY SAVINGS BANK, NEW YORK CITY

York & Sawyer, Architects Wm. H. Jackson Company, Craftsmen

(Each door approximately 5 feet 7 inches by 9 feet 8⅝ inches)

FIG. 82.—BRONZE DOORS OF COUZENS MAUSOLEUM, DETROIT, MICHIGAN
Albert Kahn, Inc., Architects   John Polachek Bronze & Iron Company, Inc., Craftsmen
A good example of the "color" possible in bronze by means of intelligent modeling, even though it be low in relief

FIG. 83.—BRONZE DOORS TO MUSEUM BUILDING, KANSAS CITY MEMORIAL
H. Van Buren Magonigle, Architect   John Polachek Bronze & Iron Company, Inc., Craftsmen
The aluminum background of the stiles and rails provides a silver foil for the applied perforated bronze ornament in relief

FIG. 85.—BRONZE ENTRANCE DOORS, HUNT-
INGTON LIBRARY, SAN MARINO, CALIFORNIA
Myron Hunt, Architect
John Polachek Bronze & Iron Co., Inc, Craftsmen

FIG. 84.—BRONZE ELEVATOR DOORS, RHODE ISLAND HOSPITAL TRUST COMPANY,
PROVIDENCE, RHODE ISLAND
York & Sawyer, Architects
Gorham Company, Craftsmen

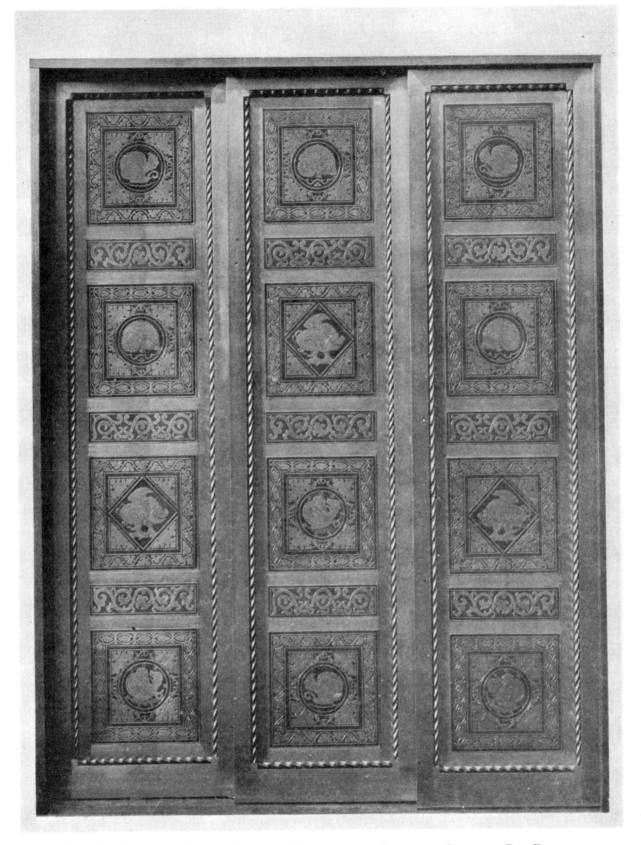

FIG. 86.—ELEVATOR DOORS, SECURITY BUILDING FOR BOSWORTH-CHANUTE CO., DENVER
W. E. & A. A. Fisher, Architects   Superb Bronze & Iron Co., Inc., Craftsmen
The ornamentation was obtained by etching, inlaying color, and then lacquering

FIG. 87.—BRONZE ENTRANCE DOORS, TENTH NATIONAL BANK, PHILADELPHIA
Davis, Dunlap & Barney, Architects   Superb Bronze & Iron Co., Inc., Craftsmen
The difficult problem of an entrance in an extremely narrow building was solved by a deep jamb reveal of black marble and bronze

FIG. 88.—BRONZE DOORS OF MAIN ENTRANCE, PARK AVENUE BUILDING, NEW YORK CITY
Buchman & Kahn, Architects   General Bronze Corporation, Craftsmen
This is one of the best examples of the manner *moderne* in America, and shows with what aptitude bronze will lend itself to this style

FIG. 89.—STANDARD SAVINGS & LOAN ASSOCIATION, UNION COMPANY OF DETROIT, DETROIT
George D. Mason & Company, Architects   Superb Bronze & Iron Co., Inc., Craftsmen
A bronze and glass partition which attains distinction by an unusual disposition of ornament and quality of composition

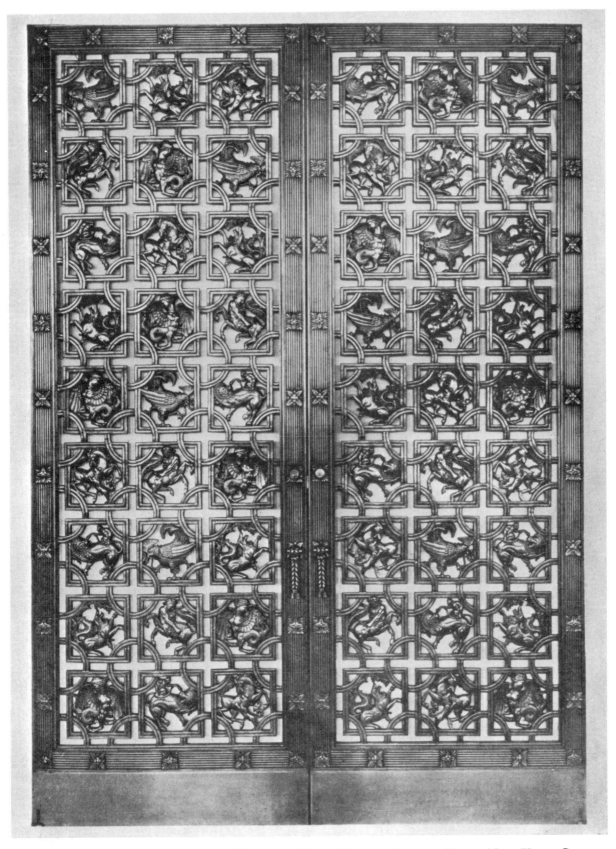

FIG. 90.—BRONZE GRILLE DOORS, ENTRANCE HALL, BOWERY SAVINGS BANK, NEW YORK CITY
York & Sawyer, Architects   Wm. H. Jackson Company, Craftsmen
Not only is the general design particularly admirable, but the pleasing variation of the modeling within each unit as well.

FIG. 93.—SECURITY TRUST CO.,
DETROIT
Albert Kahn, Inc., Architects
Superb Bronze & Iron Co., Craftsmen

FIG. 92.—C. D. PEACOCK COMPANY, CHICAGO, ILLINOIS

Holabird & Roche, Architects   Gorham Company, Craftsmen

FIG. 91.—UNION CO. OF DETROIT,
DETROIT
George D. Mason & Co., Architects
Superb Bronze & Iron Co., Craftsmen

Fig. 94.—Bronze Grilles of Revolving Door, Jewelry Shop in Straus Building, Chicago

Graham, Anderson, Probst & White, Architects   John Polachek Bronze & Iron Co., Inc., Craftsmen

FIG. 96.—BRONZE MARQUISE AND CRESTING, SHERIDAN SHOP,
FIFTH AVENUE, NEW YORK CITY
Carrère & Hastings, Architects   Tiffany Studios, Craftsmen

FIG. 95.—BRONZE SHOW WINDOW, STRAWBRIDGE & CLOTHIER,
MARKET STREET, PHILADELPHIA, PA.
Louis H. Friedland, Architect   Superb Bronze & Iron Co, Inc, Craftsmen

FIG. 97.—TICKET BOOTH, METROPOLITAN THEATRE, METROPOLITAN BUILDING, BOSTON
Blackall, Clapp & Whittemore, Architects   Gorham Company, Craftsmen

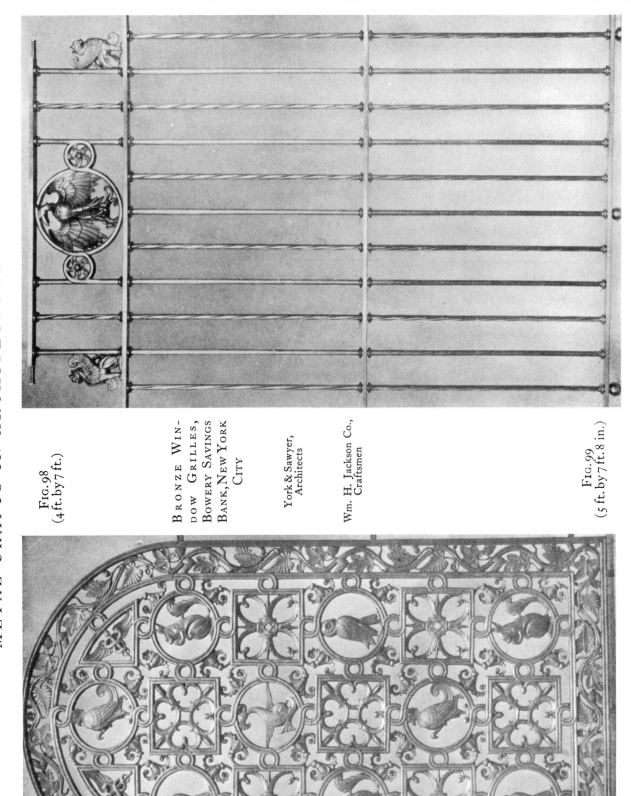

FIG. 98
(4 ft. by 7 ft.)

BRONZE WIN-
DOW GRILLES,
BOWERY SAVINGS
BANK, NEW YORK
CITY

York & Sawyer,
Architects

Wm. H. Jackson Co.,
Craftsmen

FIG. 99
(5 ft. by 7 ft. 8 in.)

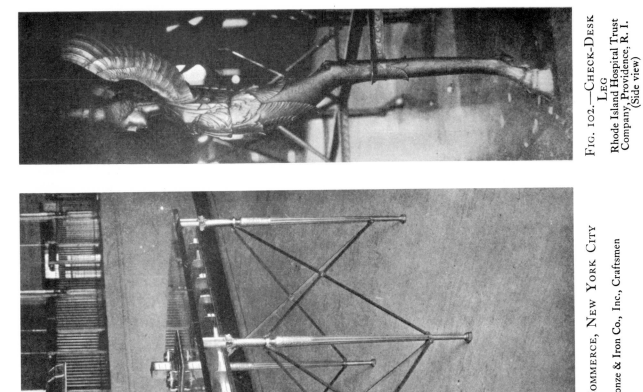

FIG. 100.—CHECK-DESK
LEG
York & Sawyer, Architects
Gorham Co., Craftsmen
(See Fig. 102)

FIG. 101.—CHECK DESK, NATIONAL BANK OF COMMERCE, NEW YORK CITY

York & Sawyer, Architects   Superb Bronze & Iron Co., Inc., Craftsmen

FIG. 102.—CHECK-DESK
LEG
Rhode Island Hospital Trust
Company, Providence, R. I.
(Side view)

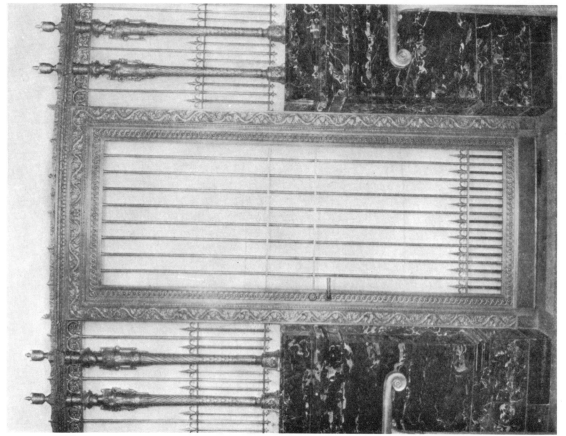

FIG. 103 (LEFT) AND FIG. 104 (RIGHT).—DOOR AND TYPICAL WICKET IN BRONZE COUNTER-SCREEN, GREENWICH SAVINGS BANK, NEW YORK CITY
York & Sawyer, Architects
John Polachek Bronze & Iron Co, Inc, Craftsmen
This counter-screen is of interest because of the continuous "deal-plate" formed by the marble instead of the more usual narrow glass plate, thus allowing for more than one teller

BRONZE: ILLUSTRATIONS

FIG. 105.—TYPICAL COUNTER-SCREEN UNIT SHOWING TELLER'S WICKET, BOWERY SAVINGS BANK, NEW YORK CITY
York & Sawyer, Architects
Wm. H. Jackson Company, Craftsmen
Another type of "deal-plate" than the one shown on the page opposite, this one being of glass at the teller's wicket; it is the more usual of the two

FIG. 108.—RHODE ISLAND
HOSPITAL TRUST CO.,
PROVIDENCE, R. I.
York & Sawyer, Architects
Gorham Company, Craftsmen

FIG. 107.—COUNTER-SCREEN, FEDERAL TRUST COMPANY, NEWARK, N. J.
Dennison & Hirons, Architects; George E. Jones, Associated Architect
Superb Bronze & Iron Co., Inc., Craftsmen

FIG. 106.—COUNTER-SCREEN,
GUARANTY TRUST CO., NEW
YORK CITY
York & Sawyer, Architects
Wm. H. Jackson Co., Craftsmen

FIG. 109.—BRONZE COUNTER-SCREEN, BROOKLYN TRUST COMPANY, BROOKLYN
York & Sawyer, Architects
Wm. H. Jackson Company, Craftsmen
Although scarcely in evidence in this reproduction, there are beautifully modeled and executed arabesques on the small twisted columns

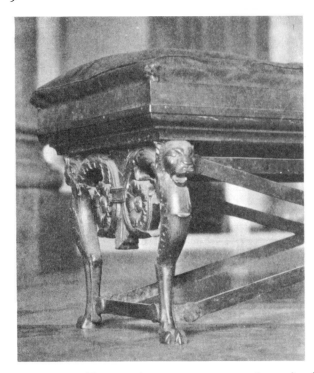

Fig. 110 (left) and Fig. 111 (right).—Bronze Ends of Banking Room Seats

Rhode Island Hospital Trust Company, Providence, R. I.

Gorham Company, Craftsmen   York & Sawyer, Architects

Greenwich Savings Bank, New York City

John Polachek Bronze & Iron Co., Inc., Craftsmen

Fig. 112.—Bronze Gate, Standard Savings & Loan Association, Union Company of Detroit

George D. Mason & Co., Architects   Superb Bronze & Iron Co., Inc., Craftsmen

FIG. 113.—BRONZE PLAQUE, "WATER," BY PAUL MANSHIP, SCULPTOR

AMERICAN TELEPHONE AND TELEGRAPH COMPANY, NEW YORK CITY

Welles Bosworth, Architect   Wm. H. Jackson Company, Craftsmen

FIG. 114.—BRONZE FLOOR-SEAL, CUNARD BUILDING, NEW YORK CITY. (17 FEET 5 INCHES DIAMETER)

Benjamin W. Morris, Architect   John Gregory, Sculptor   Gorham Company, Craftsmen

FIG. 115.—BRONZE TRAFFIC TOWER, FIFTH AVENUE, NEW YORK CITY
J. H. Freedlander, Architect   John Polachek Bronze & Iron Co., Inc., Craftsmen

BRASS

HISTORY

THE history of brass is so closely linked to that of bronze (from which it differs chemically only in the absence of tin, brass being an alloy of copper and zinc only), that it is difficult to disassociate the two. Much which in the past has been considered bronze might on analysis prove to be brass, particularly in the case of the old doors of the Romanesque period which were covered by *repoussé* plates mounted on wood stiles and panels. In Egyptian usage allusions to brass date to about 1600 B.C., when not only utensils and minor forms were fashioned from it, but brass-like drain pipes hundreds of feet long led from an upper to a lower temple in the reign of Tut-ankhaman's father. The Old Testament is full of references to brass. In succeeding periods when it is difficult to distinguish brass from bronze the subject is considered under the chapter on "Bronze" (pages 7–19). The discussion in this chapter will be briefly confined to the so-called "monumental brasses" which were popularly used for tomb slab enrichment.

From the fourteenth through the sixteenth centuries, in France, northern Germany, Belgium, and particularly England, it became the vogue to let into the stone slab covering a floor tomb, a brass plate having engraved on it the figure of the deceased, and sometimes an accompanying background of diaper design. The manufacture of the unornamented brass plates, usually rectangular in shape, centred chiefly at Cologne from where they were shipped to Belgium and England. Some examples were magnificently decorated and were as large as 5 or 6 by 10 or 12 feet. These brasses found favor with the guilds, many of the provincial ones being responsible for certain peculiarities in style and design. Not much supervision seems to have attended the letting into the stone, for many of the brass plates are upside down, due to the illiteracy of the mason. Leading draftsmen often supplied the designs. The artistic pinnacle was attained in the Gothic period.

Unfortunately there is scarcely a single brass remaining to exemplify French characteristics. It is known however that the early ones were used with Limoges enamels, *i. e.*, champlevé colors fused between thin metal ridges (page 179). The color inlay was used to depict heraldic devices and armorial details with the figure left in plain brass. This expensive method of decoration was, of course, ill-suited to the wear and tear of a floor pavement.

Of few metals is there recorded as complete a history as that of the monumental brasses in England, from the reign of Edward I (1272–1307) through all the various political upheavals until the establishment of the Commonwealth (1649). Concerning the importance of the brasses in this respect, the "Oxford Manual of Monumental Brasses" states: "A careful survey of a series of the monumental brasses of this country would enable one to follow the gradual changes of manners and habits, to track the prominent feelings, and even to detect the religious emotions, peculiar to each age; for, not only the figure, its attitude, and costume, but the inscription, and the subordinate parts of the design, all conspire to furnish a lively picture of the individual and his times." This complete record owes its preservation largely to the natural resistance of brass both to the tourist's penknife and, equally important, to fire. In support of the latter is the discovery by the Surrey Architectural Society of a beautiful little tomb brass, originally from Netley Abbey, doing service, still undamaged, as a fire-back in a cottage. Brass tomb plates were used chiefly by the middle-class, stone effigies being reserved for only persons of high rank. Although brasses suffered from fire, Puritanism, and the ravages of time less than almost any other form of ecclesiastical decoration, a large number were destroyed during the Reformation because of being too "popish"; others were sacrificed in the manufacture of cannon. Some on being taken up have older engraving on their under side.

The earliest brasses, those of the fourteenth century, are the best as regards material, boldness of design, and accuracy of ornament. As a result they are in better condition at the present than many later examples. The early designs were imitations of sculptural effigies on a flat surface, with the figure recumbent, the head on a helmet or pillow, and a lap dog or lion at the feet. Canopies were sometimes introduced into the background designs. In the fifteenth century the size of the plates not only decreased gradually, but exaggerated forms of the costume were portrayed. Both men and women were shown in profile so as to be able to depict huge head-dresses within the confines of the plate. Sometimes instead of the figure reclining, a standing posture was shown, with grass and flowers underfoot. Instead of the person being delineated with garments, an emaciated corpse, and less often a skeleton, was occasionally engraved. Shroud brasses were most common in the reign of Henry VII (1485–1509); the shroud was knotted at the hands and feet, and left open to expose the breast and knees. Frequently the brasses were

laid down during a person's life as a reminder of his mortality. Shading was accomplished by cross-hatching. In the sixteenth century the size of the plates became even smaller than in the preceding century and were often let into the walls of the church instead of the floor, as memorial tablets. Main figures were frequently shown kneeling with children grouped behind. Except for the clergy the inscriptions were in the English language common to the time. The plates were not only too thin but were composed of cheap metal. There was an excess of shading and an attempt at portraiture. The latest example of 1773 is a most decadent form of engraving with the lines barely scratched.

Photographs by Percy Simms

FIG. 116.—WILLIAM CREVEL, CHIP-
PING CAMPDEN CHURCH, 1401

FIG. 117.—GREAT TEW CHURCH,
OXFORDSHIRE

FIG. 118.—DEERHURST
CHURCH, ABOUT 1520

ENGLISH FLOOR BRASSES

CHARACTERISTICS, USAGES, CARE AND COLORING

THE word "brass" probably connotes more other names for different combinations of copper and zinc, than does any other single metal term for any group of related alloys. Some of the many designations given at various times are: laton (also latone, laiton, or latten), pinch-beck (from the inventor's name), tombac, Corinthian metal, prince's metal, ormolu (imitation gold), mo-

saic gold, similor, *electrum*, *gang gold*, etc., and, by ancient writers, *orichalcum* and *aurichalcum*.

The relative proportions of copper and zinc vary according to the purpose and color desired. Hard yellow brass, which may be wrought when cold, is generally stated as having 70 parts of copper to 30 of zinc; red brass, 80 copper to 20 zinc; brass wire (which must be tenacious and somewhat ductile), 70 copper, a small amount of lead and the remainder zinc; cast brass, from 30 to 40 per cent zinc, although the best proportion is 65 copper and 35 zinc. The particular usage for which the metal is intended determines the proportion of one metal to the other, as for plumbing, instruments, exposure to salt water, etc.

The chief physical properties of brass which are of interest architecturally are: it casts easily, is highly resistant to corrosion (although not as much so as bronze), is easier to form as the copper content increases, can be annealed so as to become soft and workable after becoming hard and brittle from beating, is relatively cheap to cast, is stronger than cast metals such as lead, and takes on high polishes and varied colors. Because it corrodes, however, it is not as suitable as bronze for either interior or exterior architectural employment unless electroplated.

When brass is finished in its natural state it must either be constantly cleaned and polished, or be electroplated, in order to withstand atmospheric action which produces an unpleasant blackish tarnish. In time the patina may turn green under certain circumstances or with the proper chemical encouragement. Every housewife knows the labor and attention required to secure and retain a high polish. Brass may be electroplated with gold or silver, and may be quite satisfactory if the plating be heavy and of first-class workmanship; whenever this is done the screws or auxiliary parts should be similarly treated, or the unsightly effect of unplated parts turning another color will sooner or later appear. Lacquering is sometimes resorted to, as for extruded sections, usually termed "extruded bronze" (page 33). This however is but a temporary cure, for the best application cannot be expected to last for longer than two or three years. The upkeep of lacquering in completely removing the remains of an under-coat and applying a new coat—at best only a makeshift for electroplating—may in the long run prove more expensive with a less desirable effect all the while, than the initial expense of electrolysis. Unfortunately, in this day of building speculation any saving of materials, whether or not shortsighted, finds great favor with the speculator who invests his money only until a buyer is found, preferably before lacquer or any other temporary finish has become tarnished and spotted. If the brass is to be used without protective covering its constant care must be

an understood obligation; if daily attention will be conscientiously accorded it, artistic potentialities abound in the color and high polish possible, as in parts of elevator cabs, push-bars on doors, hardware, ornaments about the fireplace and the like. Only if proper care be given polished brass is it an asset, for if the green-black residue of the cleaning agent be left in the depressions and around the edges, the effect is anything but desirable. Before employing it in a design the architect is the best judge as to whether or not his client will have the means and patience to keep the brass in proper fettle.

The casting process of brass is no different from that for bronze (pages 21–26), and what can be executed in one metal can be similarly done in the other. The elements of design which govern the latter, discussed in the chapter on "Bronze," refer to brass as well, and there is no gain in repetition. Parts may be similarly joined by brazing; in brass, borax is used as a flux, the metal is heated with a torch and brass solder in crystallized form is added as necessary. "Chasing" is done as for bronze, and in the same measure becomes the expensive item in the production of a first-class job. A possibility of brass (absent in bronze) is that sheets of it may be stamped with most delicate detail (without undercuts, of course), and then plated with gold or silver preparatory to being used as applied ornamentation. Besides being stamped, sheets may also be beaten out by the *repoussé* method.

As far as the architect is concerned, the conditions affecting brass do not vary from those of bronze in the matter of detailing, specifications or time allowance. Estimating plans and specifications should contain equal clarity in order to assure accurate bidding. The time necessary for the casting of bronze (page 29) can with safety be allowed for brass as well, since the operations are identical in all steps; only the contents of the crucibles vary, as the component metals are melted into fluid form.

Brass will assimilate a number of color effects, as blue, black, "hardware green," and verde antique. Accomplishing this is a specialist's job, but if the architect or his client would care to experiment, the methods of procedure can be secured in a booklet sent gratis by the Copper & Brass Research Association, 25 Broadway, New York City. How brass may be cleaned or "pickled," as the trade term has it, is also contained in the same pamphlet.

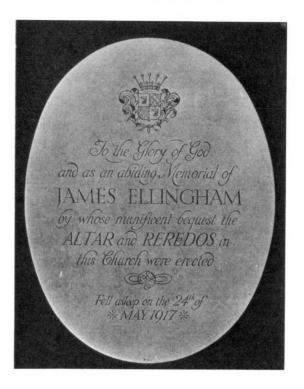

Photograph by Percy Simms

Photograph by Percy Simms

FIG. 119.—BRASS LECTERN
Church near Banbury

FIG. 120.—BRASS WITH INCISED (V) LETTERS
The Birmingham Guild, Craftsmen

FIG. 121.—BRASS LECTERN
Chipping Campden Church

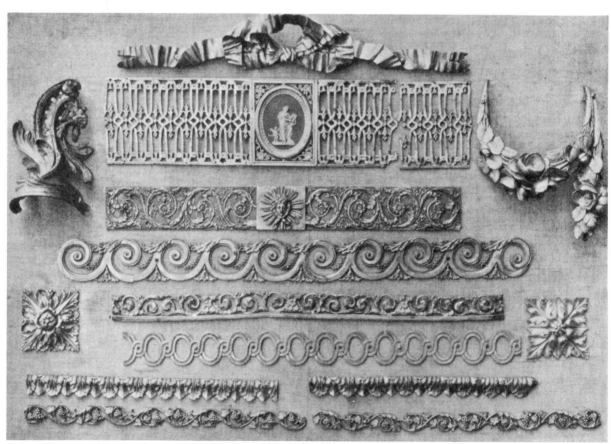

Courtesy of Metropolitan Museum of Art

FIG. 122.—BRASS MOUNTS FROM EIGHTEENTH-CENTURY FRENCH FURNITURE

FIG. 123.—FRENCH ORMOLU AND GILT BRONZE, LATE EIGHTEENTH AND EARLY
NINETEENTH CENTURIES

Figs. 123 and 124, courtesy of Metropolitan Museum of Art

FIG. 124.—BRASS MOUNTS FROM EIGHTEENTH-CENTURY FRENCH FURNITURE

FIG. 125.—BRASS HANDLES, PULLS AND ESCUTCHEONS, MOSTLY AMERICAN. (1650–1850)

CAST IRON: HISTORY

CAST iron probably traces its origin either to China or Japan, and is thought by some authorities to have been first used in the latter country for the casting of a chain used in bridge construction about 70 A. D. A passage in Aristotle indicates that the Greeks were aware that iron could be liquified by heat. M. Liger in *La Ferronrerie* notes that throughout the Greek and Roman periods iron was produced in blast furnaces. However, as far as architectural usage is concerned, there is nothing of importance known in Europe until about the fifteenth century.

The first roots of the cast iron industry in Europe date to the manufacture of pig iron in Westphalia in 1311. By 1377 German progress recorded the casting of cannon at Erfurt. A fine cast iron stove at the Castle of Coburg probably dates from 1472. In France nothing of importance seems recorded until the casting of fire-backs came into vogue with the sixteenth century. The queen's room at St. Germain had one of 1548; a number were cast in 1559 by Nicholas Clerget of St. Dizier. These and following ones usually were ornamented by emblems, ciphers and coats-of-arms.

In England cast iron became an important industry of the Weald (old English word for "forest"), located in parts of Kent, Surrey and Sussex, where the soil of clay and sandstone yielded up iron oxide. These properties were apparently discovered by the Romans, but on their departure the district was neglected. It was not until the fourteenth century that interest again seemed awakened, when one Jhone Colins provided his grave in the Burwash church with a cast iron slab, inscribed in Lombardic letters beneath a fourteenth century cross. In England the first extensive use for cast iron came with the reign of Henry VII, when a demand was created for andirons and fire-backs. The former were inspired perhaps by French prototypes, which were tall and tapering, with tops often in the form of human heads and the fronts richly decorated.

The greatest impetus to the cast iron foundry business in England came after an interview which one Ralph Hogge (Hugget) had with Henry VIII in 1543, when he suggested that he be given the commission of casting cannon in iron instead of the more costly bronze as had been the precedent. Under Elizabeth the industry reached its zenith, producing principally arms and ammunition. Fire-backs were by this time growing more in favor but confined chiefly to the castles visited by the sovereign family and those of the nobility. By the time of James II andirons were falling into disuse, and for a time fire-backs of more elaborate types were imported from Holland; soon after, however, iron masters of the Weald cast similar ones from imported patterns. The timber in the district of the Weald had been prodigally wasted and its shortage, combined with royal edicts, led to the transference of the trade to South Wales. The introduction of grates for open fireplaces made ornamental fire-backs obsolete and left this particular branch of the industry to be discontinued under the Hanoverians.

"Probably there was no thought of using cast iron for railing work until the cast Sussex iron railings were fixed round St. Paul's, in 1714. Wren for some reason objected to these, and they lay in dock for four years after delivery in London. He says, 'As to the iron fence, it is so remarkable and so fresh in memory and by whose influence and importunity it was wrested from me, and the doing of it carried in a way which I venture to say will ever be condemned.' Perhaps Wren had some stately idea, to be carried out by Tijou, who left England when the cast iron was actually delivered, in 1710. It was invoiced from Lamberhurst, but part was sublet to Mayfield; and it completely surrounded the Cathedral, including seven gates, and weighing 200 tons. The price charged, 8d. per pound, was enormous, as other castings were sold for 2d.; the cost amounted to the then almost fabulous total of £11,000. Probably for this reason no other cast railing is known to have been made in the Weald. Each vertical is a massive baluster, finishing above in a four-sided spike, and at intervals there are ponderous standards of the same finish and design. Rather close imitations are at the Oxford Schools, and Cambridge Senate House, but these have a wrought bar between each pair of cast balusters. A lighter example is at St. Leonard's, Shoreditch, put up by Dance in 1740; and cast standards of similar design alternate with wrought rails around the statue of Henry VI at Eton. Meantime we must notice that Gibbs had introduced cast iron balusters in his altar-rails, as in St. Martin's Church, about 1726, with success. Cast standards of varied and enriched design,

Fig. 126.—Cast Iron German Stove, Town Hall, Augsburg

but generally balustered, soon became familiar in London railings, the rest of the bars being plain and wrought. The designs may best be studied in the squares and streets north and south of Piccadilly, also immediately north of Oxford Street, and as far east as Bloomsbury. They are considerably varied, sometimes taking a columnar form. In nearly all cases they will be found surmounted by cast iron vases, the most popular being a flask-shape with turned foot, spherical body, tapering neck and ball-

stopper. This is rivalled by an Italian gadrooned vase on a foot, both forms introduced by Tijou. There are other forms of vase, but more rarely seen until the Adam style prevailed. Besides the vase, a ball finial is sometimes used, or a mace-head design with fluted umbrella-shaped top over a spreading base, as seen in Whitehall Yard and Gwydyr House, 1796; the pine cone and the acorn, the former at Kensington Palace and near the Horse Guards, and the latter in Cheyne Row and Serjeants' Inn; they occur together in Upper Brook Street. A curious cast design of two moulded scrolls meeting under a flask-like knob became a cheap substitute for wrought finials on gates, to be seen on those of St. John's College, Cambridge, and elsewhere; and these occasionally replace vases on railings, as in Serjeants' Inn and on the north side of Clapham Common." *

In the United States cast iron acquitted itself creditably except perhaps during the latter half of the nineteenth century, when lack of discriminating taste in design gave the foundry man but rare opportunities to make a creditable showing. Great numbers of firebacks were produced from about 1740–'60, particularly in Pennsylvania by German settlers. Many bear scriptural quotations or terse moralizing admonitions; the modeling possessed a vigorous quality in most cases, not lacking in humor. As an architectural adjunct of an ornamental nature, after initial employment as fire-backs, cast iron was used as in England in conjunction with wrought iron. Many examples occur in the railings and gates of the early days of the Republic and continue into the beginning of the second quarter of the nineteenth century (pages 118–125). The Greek Revival led to even greater usage of the combination of cast and wrought iron, in many cases with a predominance of cast work. In the South more often than in the North there was a fondness exhibited for reproducing a vine growth, particularly for porches (pages 120 and 123).

New Orleans in particular can boast of aristocratic cast iron forebears. The material was introduced about the Directoire and Empire periods of France, in enriching wrought designs with cast ornaments. Later, after American domination had well established itself, the district above Canal Street found itself displaying cast designs in entirety. The introduction of cast iron invited a type of balcony which ex-

* J. Starkie Gardner, "Ironwork," III.

tended to the edge of the street by spanning the sidewalk, and was protected overhead by a roof; however, while the ornament was cast, the structural members were usually wrought. The earliest castings were restrained in design, with mouldings harking back to Spanish grilles in some cases, and adaptations of Louis XVI in others. The second quarter of the nineteenth century witnessed a wider use of cast ornament than in the previous period, a movement which led to a florid development by the mid-century. The fondness of New Orleans architects for tying together various units of a *parti* led to the extensive employment of brick or stone walls, and later to cast iron fences. Few of these still survive in the old French Quarter except around Jackson Square, but more are extant in the "new" American Quarter, or the Garden District. A fondness prevailed for enclosing public squares and parks in the European manner, but neglect and "progress" have unfortunately combined to lessen their numbers year by year.

The retrogradation in taste after the Civil War affected cast iron as it did everything else, and much was executed which had been better uncast. The gradual architectural Renaissance, begun in the '90's and in large measure due to the leadership of McKim, Mead & White, improved the quality of cast iron among other building materials, and started cast iron on its most prosperous period, continuing until the World War. Among the many cast iron foundries then flourishing, the best known and parent to many others was the Hecla Company of Brooklyn, which only recently closed its plant. Unfortunately there has been no complete photographic record of its work in monographic form, although there is a good collection of representative photographs at the Science Room of the New York Public Library.

Since the World War the introduction of terra-cotta, tile, brick, etc., for spandrels has greatly reduced the amount of cast iron previously used for that purpose; the increased capital being spent on commercial buildings has led to the wider usage of bronze for entrances and particularly for banking counterscreens. Also, the reputation of cast iron has in many quarters suffered from the mediocre workmanship which numbers of inferior foundries have turned out, to the discomfiture of the better firms unwilling to produce anything

Photograph by Richard Koch

FIG. 127.—CAST IRON GATES AND FENCE, JACKSON SQUARE, NEW ORLEANS

but first-class craftsmanship. The future of the industry in ornamental cast iron work is dependent in a large measure upon the interest and training of the architect, his power of per-

Courtesy of the Pennsylvania Museum, Memorial Hall, Philadelphia

FIG. 128.—CAST IRON STOVE PLATE, PENNSYLVANIA-GERMAN, 1741

suasion with the client to allow only first-class foundries the privilege of estimat ng, and his rightful exercise of authority in rejecting unsatisfactory castings at the foundry and unsightly erection at the building.

CAST IRON: CRAFTSMANSHIP

SEVERAL decades ago when the practice of architecture was not the complicated endeavor it has now become through the growing importance of mechanical equipment and real estate machinations, an architect had time to devote to cast iron. With the increased and manifold demands on his time and energy, however, cast iron has been more and more disregarded with no uncertain results, in being less and less of a credit to itself, the foundry, the architect and the building. In the present era of specialization, where one of the architect's henchmen designs the iron at small scale, another full-sizes it, and another may (but seldom if ever does) inspect it at the foundry, it is only the natural result that the iron foundries on the whole have done less meritorious work than twenty years ago.

The critical eye of the architect no longer has time to be interested in iron in the making. His job is to sign contracts, see to their execution, and keep the clients jovial. There is no "spare" time either in his preliminary training or in his practice to learn more than the elementary facts about cast iron. Most regrettable of all is the shocking ignorance of many architects as to what cast iron can and should be, what the material is capable of, and what the client is entitled to. The splendid work of the old Hecla Company, Brooklyn, stands as a monument to what cast iron may achieve; unfortunately the foundry has lately gone out of business, but the high quality of its craftsmanship still serves as a stimulus to the better foundries now practising. Were the architect to caution his foundry that he expected Hecla quality, and know what that meant, his client would not have to accept solidified Swiss cheese surfaces painted over. Unfortunately, however, many organizations know little and care less concerning the fate of their cast iron designs, once the shop-drawings have been checked and out of the way. By the time the iron is ready for delivery, the owner wants more than anything else to move in and collect revenue from rents; he would be entirely out of sympathy with any rejection of cast iron work which would delay the swelling of his bank account. At that stage of a building it is futile for the architect to blame poor cast iron work on anyone but himself, for had his details been issued on time, and the shop-drawings promptly checked, he might have demanded that the iron be cast far enough in advance so that it could be inspected at the foundry. A foundry requires the greatest time on the work in the preparation up to the point where the mould can be poured; if the casting turns out poorly it is only a matter of another day to pour another one, and if the architect inspects its quality *then*, there will be no reason for honeycombed surfaces on delivery at the building.

The architect interested in obtaining a creditable cast iron job can with but little effort determine which foundries are doing first-class work. There are not many and we are tempted to mention them, but inadvertently might omit some worthy ones. With one accord the foundries anxious to cast in a craftsmanlike manner report that their greatest sales obstacle is the education of the architect to the differences between a good casting with smooth surfaces and invisible joints, and a poor one full of flaws and unsightly fittings. What can a conscientious cast iron craftsman reply to an architect who complacently views a frightful piece of workmanship with the remark, "Well, that's what you expect of cast iron." Not all architects are of that calibre of course; many, on being compelled to accept bids from mediocre foundries, have become so discouraged with results in spite of unflagging interest, that they have chosen to eliminate cast iron wherever possible. Certain of the best architect's offices, on receiving bids for bronze work which exceed what the client can afford, redesign the elements in non-metallic material if possible, rather than resort to cast iron. The best craftsmen in cast iron, as in bronze, unite in deprecating the discreditable workmanship by some of the foundries, a condition which decreases the amount of business they might otherwise do—gradual dissatisfaction on the part of architects and public is bound to react in diminishing usage. On the other hand, lack of understanding on the part of the architect results in indefinite specifications and poor drawings, followed by unfair bidding in favor of the poorest craftsman, which culminates in erected work which is a discredit not only to the foundry but to the architect as well.

Even the architect too busy to acquaint

himself with the characteristics of cast iron design and the difference between such foundry terms as "cope" and "drag," should at least appreciate the simple differences between what may reasonably be expected of an iron casting compared to a bronze one. The foundry problems may not interest him (although they necessarily put limitations on his draftsmen's designs), but he should know how iron is best painted. He can scarcely neglect realizing that cast iron can usually be erected without a screwhead showing on an exposed face, that in exceptional cases where necessary these should not interfere with the ornamentation, and that the heads should be countersunk deeply enough so that putty will completely fill the hole flush before being painted over. He should know that plain surfaces can be cast *without* surface irregularities and *with* true edges. If he does not concern himself about shrinkage (usually taken to be ⅛-inch to the foot), he may experience an embarrassing situation at the building because castings do not fit, although made directly from accurate models which he approved. He should ascertain whether the foundry will cast metal patterns from the models directly, and if so, should make certain that his modeler makes a *double* shrinkage allowance. If castings do not fit because of the shrinkage loss being forgotten, the architect has no one to blame but himself, no matter how zealous he may be to transfer the blame to the contractor.

The future quality of cast iron ornamentation depends largely on the concerted policy of the architectural profession. On the whole the indifference in the past to premier quality has invited unfair, dishonest and inferior competition. Some foundries have discontinued business rather than stoop to uncraftsmanlike work; others have forsaken ornamental work for structural and commercial products. A continuance would mean that as the better cast iron foundries lose heart and the amount of creditable workmanship steadily decreases, either the architects must accept inferior products without recourse, or be forced to do without cast iron entirely. Often no doubt it has not been intentional negligence on the part of most architects never to have become informed concerning cast iron, but has been rather one of those habitual procrastinations which are classed as "artistic license." Then too, there is but little available library information in easily accessible sources, and unless the architect be of an unusual nature, he will attend 10 concerts and 100 theatres in his prized opportunities for relaxation, before once seeking out a single cast iron foundry. In recognition of these conditions there follows a brief summary of the processes which take place within the mysterious confines of a cast iron plant.

THE ESSENTIALS OF IRON CASTING

PROBABLY every architect who has been satisfied with bronze has at one time or another been dissatisfied with cast iron, and has asked a question of the iron foundry which has a variety of answers: "Why don't you use French sand and bake the moulds so as to get the sharp definition of bronze?" Presidents, treasurers, shop-foremen, moulders—whoever may be interrogated—all have different replies. From a shop-practice standpoint there is nothing against using baked French sand moulds for cast iron, providing they are properly "vented" for the greater quantity of escaping gases as compared with bronze; in this manner undercutting on a small scale could be obtained, as well as practically the same sharpness of ornament. However, if such were done the casting might better be executed in bronze for several reasons: bronze has a lower melting point than iron and because of greater fluidity does not set as quickly, consequently it duplicates the surfacing of the mould more conscientiously, and shows a better return for the amount of labor expended; when the casting has cooled, the ornament in bronze can be refined by "chasing," while in iron nothing can be done to it; the only additional expense to the client for bronze would be the cost of the raw material, which would scarcely be much more than for iron when the upkeep-cost of the latter is added. In a word, if baked sand moulds were to be used for iron castings, the expense of bronze ones would almost be reached, without the advantages of the latter. Generally iron is employed instead of bronze because of lower price, whereas if baked sand moulds instead of "green" sand moulds are resorted to, it can be understood from the foregoing explanation that this purpose is defeated. The architect, in all fairness to his client, should familiarize himself with what first-class cast iron should be, and then use it within the natural limitations of the material. What comprise these latter can better be understood by following through the various steps in the development of a casting from blue prints to erection, before considering "Characteristics Affecting Design" (pages 114-115).

The complete account of ornamental iron casting should antedate the signing of the contract by the sub-contractor. For the best results it should date back—both for the sake of quality of work and maximum return for the amount spent—to the development of architect's sketches into working drawings, when a reputable foundry man was called into the architect's drafting-room for advice. Even for the architect who has used iron extensively there is seldom a problem which exactly repeats itself or which will not bear constructional improvement. Good design admittedly is based on sound construction, yet an architect who has never ventured near a foundry can scarcely be expected to have more than a hazy notion of what good construction in cast iron may be. Moreover, it not infrequently happens that a good cast iron contractor can simplify the details in such a way as not only to produce a better condition for casting at a lower price, but the very simplification may lead to better design. If, after the contract has been awarded, the same cast iron man should make the same suggestion, the architect would mentally make note that "here is another one of those 'subs' out to make a killing." So often has the architect been aware that changes in his details have been for the sole purpose of making profits for the contractor, that when a bona fide suggestion for the improvement of the job is made, he is wary as a fox. Some offices are reticent about calling in contractors for information lest the latter insert some peculiarity which will make the work easier for themselves and harder for their competitors—which is another way of admitting that having so little information at first-hand about cast iron, the architect is suspicious of anything which any one tells him about it. If such be the case, the architect's best recourse is to familiarize himself with foundry practice. There is probably not a cast iron foundry in the country which would not welcome any architect's visit at any time, no matter how inconvenient it might be; conducting him through the plant might result in a

loss of time to the foundry but it would be a gain to the architect. A lack of knowledge on the part of the architect is nobody's liability but his own. If his working drawings cost him excessively, if the estimates run too high so that much work must be eliminated, if the final result as installed in place at the building is slovenly and the client is displeased, there is only one reason and only one solution. The brief description which follows cannot begin to serve as a substitute for a visit to a foundry; it is hoped that it may convey an idea of the stages preliminary to the production of a casting, the limitations of the material, some of the problems met by the plant, and enough of an account so that a foundry visit may be prefaced by some understanding of the progressive steps. Perhaps, too, it may implant a desire to see the fireworks and enjoy the show.

To commence the story at the plant—we have used the word "foundry" as indicative of the entire plant, whereas actually it is only that part where the dough is prepared and the cake baked. But much happens before. Assume that the architect, in the preparation of his working drawings, has benefited by the advice of his cast iron consultant, and that the modeler also took counsel with the foundry which is to execute the work so that models were made to the proper shrinkage scale, mounted on "follow boards," and done in such a manner as to be mutually advantageous by avoiding double labor and trebled argument later. Incidentally, if the architect would save himself energy and temper, he will insert a paragraph in his specifications to insure an amiable conference between the modeler and the cast iron contractor, *holding the former responsible that models be in accordance with the requirements of foundry usage.* While the models are in preparation the foundry has prepared its shop-drawings which have been accurately and promptly (?) checked by the architect's office. When the models and checked shop-drawings have reached the iron plant they are probably a month behind the schedule allowed the cast iron contractor, so that the poor fellow must lay aside all the other work in order to rush through a job which is late before he even gets a chance to begin. Were he to continue placidly with his other contracts, taking the job in its order, and later produce conclusive evidence such as contracts, letters, and dates on architectural drawings and checked shop-drawings, to prove that the architect and modeler were responsible for the original delays, the architect would commence an aria which would end as a swan song for the iron contractor. So we assume that the plant makes the best of conditions and begins work as soon as all models and checked shop drawings are received.

The ball is started rolling in the pattern shop, which is an expert carpentry organization where forms are built up in wood with the *finesse* of cabinet work. Sometimes only a single pattern is required for single-faced work, as a spandrel with flat ornament; at other times two are necessary, as for cartouches with warped surface backgrounds, and intricate high-relief ornament. The purpose of the wood patterns is to provide a shape around which the sand may be rammed, and which, when removed, will leave a space into which the molten metal can be poured. Since pouring thickness varies from ¼ to ⅜ of an inch for usual operations, it is evident that sometimes a wood pattern can be made of such thickness, while at other times needed strength in the wood requires greater thickness, as ⅞-inch, which is more than a casting should be. In that case two patterns are necessary, one to form an impression in the lower half of the flask (Figures 132, 133) and another in the upper, the latter pattern being smaller all over by ¼ to ⅜ of an inch. To begin with, a simple problem of a flat panel is assumed in Figure 129, and illustrates diagrammatically the various parts as assembled. It is here also assumed that the pattern, C, can be made of one thickness, which when withdrawn, will leave a

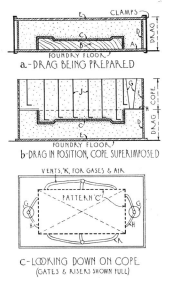

a-DRAG BEING PREPARED

b-DRAG IN POSITION, COPE SUPERIMPOSED

VENTS, 'K,' FOR GASES & AIR

PATTERN 'C'

c-LOOKING DOWN ON COPE
(GATES & RISERS SHOWN FULL)

FIG. 129

space between the top and bottom surfaces of the sand having the correct thickness for the intended casting.

The nomenclature of the various elements used to produce a cast iron mould are indicated in Figure 129, and a brief description of the successive operations follows in the ensuing paragraph.

The board which is placed on the foundry floor to form a bed for the pattern, C, is the "follow" board, A. If a supporting base is required for the pattern it may be of wood, as B, called the "bed" board. When these two are in place, a parting powder is added to the face of the pattern, C, so that later when removed none of the sand is likely to cling. Following this the pattern is "riddled" or sprinkled with facing sand, the latter being rammed firmly by degrees as it is added. Heap-sand, used for backing, is shovelled on and rammed until it becomes level with the top of the "drag," or outer enclosing frame. When the top surface is "struck" or completely levelled, the "bottom" board, E, is securely clamped to the drag and follow board. The entire portion thus formed, collectively called the "drag," is rolled over on the floor in the position shown in Figure 129-b, after which the clamps, follow board and bed board are removed. The lower half of the form is thus in readiness; to complete the operation the upper portion, collectively known as the "cope," is next formed. The proceeding is much the same as for the drag, beginning with dusting parting powder on the exposed side of the pattern, riddling the surface with facing sand, and placing the outer frame or "cope," F, in position. At this stage provision must be made for supplying a means of entrance for the molten metal. This is done by means of funnel-shaped openings termed "sprues," G, which in turn connect with horizontal grooves in the sand called "gates," H, mentioned later. The entire cope will later be lifted off for finishing, so that the sand must be reinforced by "gaggers," J, hanging bars, "soldiers" and "chucks." Heap-sand for backing is first riddled and then shovelled in, being rammed at intervals. The funnels for the formation of the sprues are withdrawn, and the entire cope is rolled over on the floor for finishing, *i. e.*, sand which might have become displaced is replaced and the surface sponged as described later. It might be mentioned that this face of exposed sand will determine the back or unseen face of the panel. Screws are then inserted in the pattern, which has retained its position, C; the pattern is then gently rapped, and withdrawn. The drag is then in readiness to be finished by having the surface (the front face of the panel) carefully restored in case the withdrawal of the pattern has disturbed any sand; then the gates, H, are grooved into the sand, radiating from the sprues. "Risers" must also be made (Figure 129-c in plan); these are grooves usually placed as far distant as possible from the point where the metal is poured into the mould; their purpose is not only to allow the gases and displaced air a means of escape, but to indicate when the mould is filled to overflowing with molten metal. The final steps remaining are only to apply sealing powder along the joints of the flask, to replace the cope and clamp it to the drag, and, if necessary on a large casting, to provide a "pouring basin," or reservoir, which will contain sufficient molten metal to flood the entire mould simultaneously.

To return for a moment to the subject of patterns. When the casting is as simple as the panel described above there may be no difficulties experienced in the pattern shop, but when there are capitals, columns, cartouches with curved surfaces, etc., it is often necessary to form two patterns, one for the drag and the other for the cope, so made that one is smaller than the other by the thickness which the metal is to be. Often these require no little skill to make, for what is simple to draw in elevation on a "full-size," may become an involved problem in descriptive geometry in the solid, which must be built up of successive layers of wood, expertly dowelled and glued together. In cases where there is much duplication of the same pattern it is sometimes advantageous to make wood patterns first from which metal patterns may be cast, since the latter will obviously better withstand the repeated punishment of ramming in the foundry flasks. In this case double-shrinkage must be taken into account, since the metal patterns will shrink first, and the final castings poured in them will do so also. For highly ornamental work, the plaster model as it comes from the modeler will often suffice as a pattern if the casting is to be single-faced, but the plaster must be well backed so that it will not crack when sand is rammed against it. This plaster pattern will serve for the drag to form the finished face of the casting, but the reverse side in the cope requires another pattern, smaller all over, to allow for the thickness of the metal, if the latter is to be of constant depth and follow the ups and downs of the ornamental face.

The problem illustrated in the marginal diagram, Figure 130, of an engaged column, is a common one which is typical of a number of similar operations requiring so-called "core prints." In *I* is shown the wood pattern, *A*, whose profile corresponds to what is eventually

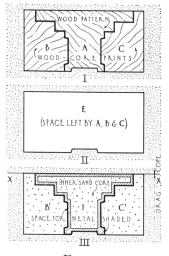

FIG. 130

desired in cast iron; *B* and *C* are wood core prints which fit exactly, the three members fitting like a solid wood mass. These are placed in the drag, and the sand is rammed firmly around them, leaving a space in the sand after their withdrawal which in section is shown by *E* in *II*. Sand cores, *B¹* and *C¹*, are then made to correspond exactly with the wood core prints, *B* and *C*. A centre core, *F*, is formed which is smaller all around than *A* by the thickness which the iron is to be. In *III* are shown the two sand cores *B¹* and *C¹*, and the inner sand core, *F*. These are placed in the drag in corresponding positions to *A*, *B*, and *C* in *I*, i. e., in the space *E* in *II*. The space between the outer and inner cores, shown cross-hatched, is that which is allowed for the molten iron to occupy. The line *X-X* indicates the line on which the cope and drag would be divided. Usual foundry practice is to have the drag, or bottom part of the flask, contain the finished or front surface of the casting, and the top part, or the cope, to contain what will be the back surface, because the slag, being lighter, rises to the top when in the fluid state. Whereas the top surface might have an occasional air or gas bubble impeding the flow of the metal, the bottom part is more likely to have all its parts filled because of gravity's helping pull.

Column patterns for the outside circumference may be in two halves if there be no flutes, but when there are flutes each half will have to be subdivided into several sections, usually three as in Figure 131. It is obvious that unless the flutes were extremely shallow, a pattern made in one piece could not be removed from the sand in the direction of arrow *a*. In order to execute semicircular flutes the pattern would be built up of three sections, *A*, *B* and *C*. *A* would be removed first in the

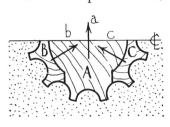

FIG. 131

direction of arrow *a*, followed by *B* and *C*, in the directions indicated by their respective arrows, *b* and *c*.

The manner in which models for double-faced ornament are usually made, studied first in clay and then in plaster of Paris when approved by the architect, often necessitates the foundry's making the models all over again in bee's or other wax, mounted on a follow board, which will follow the line of division between cope and drag. This repetition of labor not only costs the client money but loses the detail of the modeling as executed by the modeler. There seems to be no good reason for this duplication of labor, which at present leads estimators of the best firms to include an amount in their bid equivalent to the cost of making all models over. If the architect were to benefit by the experience of a cast iron consultant while his specifications were being written, he could then determine exactly what models would be required and how they should be prepared by the modeler. A saving could thus be made which for certain jobs on record amounted to several thousand dollars. In general the main thing affected is where double-faced ornament occurs. If the modeler is to supply *working* models in this case, he must either furnish: (*a*) a complete model split in the middle, made either of plaster or preferably wax; or (*b*), a solid, double-faced model of plaster or wax with a plaster follow board into which half of the model will fit—as shown in the marginal diagram, half of the model fits into the follow board

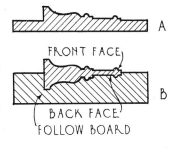

FRONT FACE

BACK FACE
FOLLOW BOARD

A

B

and the other half projects from it. Usually the architect sees only one side of any double-faced ornament, half projecting from a slab of plaster. This however cannot be used by the foundry for the making of a casting, for while it would do for one face in the cope, it would not provide for leaving an impression in the drag. For the foundry to make its own working models means a considerable loss in the sharpness of ornament, since from the modeler's model must first be made a negative, and then two positives—one for the cope and one for the drag. If this extra labor can be saved by the modeler's doing as described above, it not only spares the client the useless

extra expense, but gives the casting more nearly the definition which the architect thought he would get when he approved the plaster model in the modeler's shop. Were the modeler to furnish a complete model for both faces split down the middle, the making of the mould is a simple affair, since it resolves itself into one for the cope and the other for the drag.

The subject of follow boards is a technical consideration about which the architect need not concern himself except to insert in his specifications a proviso that, "the modeler shall confer with the cast iron contractor and furnish to his satisfaction all the models on follow boards in accordance with the details and directions furnished by the latter," and as to estimating, that "the cast iron contractor need make no allowance for remaking any models furnished him by the modeler."

The term "draft" used in moulding designates the amount of splay necessary on the sides of a pattern so that it may readily be lifted from the sand without the latter's clinging to it. The marginal diagram indicates a

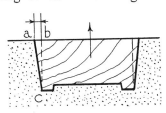

wood pattern with sand rammed around it, ready to be pulled out in the direction of the arrow. Were the side *ac* perpendicular to *ab* it would

be almost impossible to maintain a clean, sharp edge of sand at point *a*. The "draft" is the distance *ab*, but in reality this is always so slight as to be imperceptible to the eye. As a matter of practice the draft on one side is sometimes omitted if that of the side opposite is sufficient for easily removing the pattern. Both the use of the parting compound mentioned previously and the tapping of the pattern aid in its removal from the sand, so that if a right angle is absolutely necessary, it can be approximated within a fraction of a degree.

Generally speaking, cast iron is poured into unbaked or "green" sand moulds, prepared as described previously, and composed of finely grained sand, yellow in color when new but soon black from sea coal facing and usage. The finest moulding sand in the United States is said to come from glacial deposits near Saratoga along the Hudson River, and goes under the trade term of "Albany sand." It does not have the high cohesive qualities of French sand (which allows the modeler to build up a core of unbaked sand and remove it several times without crumbling in bits), and therefore imposes some restraint upon the designer who would stay within the economic confines of the material. For example, take the common garden variety of dentils, which still flourish in any and most designs even though the world is overpopulated with them. In bronze the row of dentils can be of almost any projection and the moulder's labors are not increased, because the sand cores are baked and can be withdrawn with ease. In cast iron on the other hand, dentils of equally

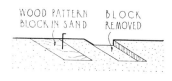

WOOD PATTERN BLOCK IN SAND BLOCK REMOVED

great depth *can* be obtained but only with added labor costs, because the wood blocks which comprise the core for each dentil must be withdrawn one at a time, having a screw turned in the back of each so that the four little walls of unbaked sand will not crumble in. Were an entire row of deep dentil blocks to be united, either the draft would necessarily have to be excessive or the edges of sand would not survive. To say that cast iron puts some restraint upon the designer is inaccurate in the sense that if the client be willing to pay the piper anything can be obtained in cast iron as well as in bronze, but the cost would be entirely out of proportion with the result. If cast iron is not considerably cheaper than bronze it would be better to use the latter. The problem actually resolves itself into the designer's understanding that he cannot economically hope to design for bronze and then label it cast iron. Each metal has its particular characteristics (those of cast iron are considered later), but it is worthy of mention at this juncture that the difference in the manner of moulding and the use of unbaked sand impose limitations which should be respected.

When the sand has been rammed against a pattern and the latter withdrawn, several precautions are taken to insure the iron's receiving a smooth surface. Where there is ornamentation of high relief, or edges which might easily crumble, or any exceptional problems where the unbaked sand might suffer from the onrush of molten metal where it has been delicately modeled, so-called "skin-drying" is often resorted to. This amounts to baking the mould in certain areas by the use of a blow-torch held near enough to the surface of the mould to dry the sand. Before the torch is applied, it should

be mentioned, the surface is treated by spraying with molasses water and dusting with black lead. Skin-drying is the exception rather than the rule, but in all cases when a pattern has been removed from the sand, the surface is sprinkled or sprayed with molasses water (inky black in color), to increase its adhesion. Following this, when the surface has dried, a moulder distributes a cloud of "black lead" dust over the entire mould's surface, which later will prevent the molten iron from "burning into the sand," as it is called. When the black lead dust has settled, a soft brush is applied over the surface with a gentle painting stroke to completely ingrain the particles, but without disturbing the modeling. In a moment or two the mould glistens like burnished pewter. A bellows puts to rout any unattached particles of sand or black lead, and the surface is in readiness for an unobstructed deluge of molten iron. The outstanding foundry mystery seems to be the fact that the sand although firmly rammed is still susceptible to a light finger imprint, and yet unfalteringly resists the onrush of molten metal to such a degree that not a grain of sand seems to be dislocated.

The casting of a column shaft is an operation necessitating no little effort in preparing the "core," *i. e.*, the amount of sand which will occupy the central space during the pouring, and which afterward becomes the hollow part of the shaft. This cylindrical core is made of two halves securely bound together. In the

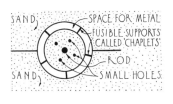

SAND SPACE FOR METAL FUSIBLE SUPPORTS CALLED 'CHAPLETS' ROD SAND SMALL HOLES

centre is a stout rod which acts as a permanent support for the core throughout its existence, surrounded by a number of lesser ones, each about an eighth inch in diameter. These remain in the core until just before pouring, when they are pulled out at the end of the flask to serve as vents for gases which accumulate in the pouring. These cores are painted with a coat of good quality "blacking" or "core wash" to insure their remaining intact. Small pieces of fusible metal, called "chaplets," support the core in the middle of the space to be poured, as shown in the marginal diagram; these eventually melt with the onrush of hot iron and become part of it, but preserve their identity long enough to hold the core in the proper position.

When both cope and drag moulds are in

readiness (surface applications of molasses water and black lead having been applied as described), the cope is carefully picked up by a travelling overhead crane if it be a big one, and turned upside down. Then, with a man guiding it at each end and giving directions to the crane-chauffeur by sounds which are like those of Venetian gondoliers and about as intelligible to the lay ear, the cope is laid to rest on top of the drag. The master of the crane is so highly sensitive that he adeptly lowers several tons of sand and several hours of labor so gently and slowly that not a grain seems misplaced. When the cope is settled in place it is clamped to the drag, the waiting mouths of the sprues are prepared for the flow of iron, and all is in readiness.

Most foundries so operate that by three or four o'clock in the afternoon the stage is set for pouring. Twenty minutes before this begins the furnace, or "cupola" as it is called, is started on its job of melting the iron. This large caldron is simply a cylindrical basin having a spout from which the metal can flow, and a device for blowing compressed air into the chamber, called "tuyères," both being fairly near the bottom, and an open top into which the iron "pigs" and coke can be dumped. The cupola is usually so arranged that it may be "charged" or loaded from the exterior of the foundry, with lifting apparatus convenient for hoisting the iron and coke. The blast of air enters at the tuyères and must be continuous; a cessation of the air supply would result in the melting having to be discontinued for the day, the bottom of the cupola having to be dropped, and the furnace cooled so that repairs could be made. Air under about a pound of pressure is supplied from a source having two systems, so that there is diminished danger of a break in the draft. The loading of the cupola is a technical problem in metallurgy of no interest to the layman, except that the contents in general are alternate layers of coke and iron, with some flux or oyster-shells thrown on top to collect the slag. The inside of the cupola is lined with fire-brick which is daubed with fireclay for a thickness of several inches. At the bottom and front of the cupola, opening into the foundry, is an aperture about 6 inches in diameter called the "breast," just below which is a spout extending at an incline for a distance of about 3 feet. Before the cupola fire is started the workman in charge places an iron rod in the 6-inch diameter hole or breast, and packs dry fireclay around it, and when

completely filled up withdraws the iron rod. In his hands he then rolls several moist clay plugs which will fit the small hole remaining, and sticks these plugs on the ends of 10-foot long iron pikes.

When the moulds are in readiness for pouring the excitement is about to begin. The blast is started and in from ten to twelve minutes

FIG. 132

Views in a cast iron foundry, showing the finished cope of a curved door pediment, being carried and lowered by an overhead crane, preparatory to being let down on the drag (Fig. 133)

FIG. 133

in some foundries, and eighteen to twenty minutes in others, the liquid metal begins to trickle out of the small hole into the spout, and is caught by a receptacle called an "exterior mixing ladle." The condition of the melting iron is observed, the aperture is stopped up by one of the clay plugs on the end of a long pike, and the mixture is allowed to continue to collect in the cupola for about ten minutes more, at which time the first iron is drawn off for pouring.

At any time when a foundry is in its over-

FIG. 134

This view taken at the cupola shows the molten iron flowing into
an exterior mixing ladle, in front of which is a small ladle with characteristic handles. The tuyères of the cupola can be seen projecting to right and left of the breast, the aperture from which the iron
is flowing. The workman in charge of the cupola is at the right
with a pike and a barb of moist clay on its tip

alls it is an engaging show staged amid murky
sets, enlivened by spooklike cranes drifting
mysteriously along with weird prey in their
claws, and workers scurrying like so many
black ants rebuilding a destroyed hill. But on
a winter's night when the only light of importance comes from sputtering ladles and the
glowing vents and sprues, which have done
their jobs and are cooling off in a sullen manner, it is as exciting as a war manœuvre, and
as colorful as the burning of Rome. When the
iron is "right" to be poured, the workman who
officiates at the cupola places the exterior mix-

FIG. 135

This mould requires the pouring of four ladles simultaneously.
Molten iron can be seen flowing into the sprues; puttees and
goggles used as precautionary measures are also in evidence

ing ladle at the bottom of the spout, seizes a
long pike and with unerring aim shatters the
plug in the cupola breast. Out jumps the liv-
ing gold. It comes stumbling and hurtling out,
as if thankfully freed from further Inquisitorial-
boiling. When the exterior mixing ladle, which
acts as a temporary reservoir, is sufficiently
filled, the Dead-eye-Dick person again seizes a
pike, barbs it with a moist clay plug, and stops
the flow of iron. Two men then take positions
fore and aft of a small ladle, which will hold
perhaps 150 pounds of the molten iron, and
place it so that it can be filled from the exterior
mixing ladle which just received a supply from
the cupola. When their ladle is filled they
hasten off with it, to dump it in a waiting sprue,
if it be a small casting, or otherwise wait until
several more of their confrères also have their
ladles filled and are standing at attention ready
to pour the contents simultaneously down the
several gullets of a large casting. In addition
to the two men who carry and pour each ladle,
is a third workman who skims the slag from the
surface with a rod. When the poured metal
has filled every possible crevice of the mould
it rises in the sprues and risers, and unless the
workmen are alert, may even overflow the top.
Bubbling, spattering iron burns cruelly, and as
a protective measure many states have invoked
laws requiring the wearing of goggles and
leather puttees. Many of the old hands, however, wear the goggles as if to protect their
bald pates instead of their eyes, and look more
like peculiar two-legged beetles with stunted
antennæ, than serious ladlers of golden iron.
When a pair of workmen has some of the contents of the ladle still remaining after the latest
mould has been surfeited, they take it back to
the exterior mixing ladle and empty it therein.
Then all wait in line until the big ladle is again
filled and they have a new assignment given
them. One mould after another is poured until
all have been satiated. Usually the foundry
foreman has been able to estimate so accurately
the amount of fluid iron needed, that after the
last mould has been poured the contents of the
cupola are practically drained. The dregs are
poured into shallow, parallel depressions in the
floor, called the "pig bed," and when cool can
be used to feed the cupola the day following.
    Another word on the pageantry of the pour-
ing: when the mould is filled and the surplus
metal rises and overflows, not only do a few
main sprues, gates and risers burn and glow
merrily, but hundreds of little gas jets, fed

by escaping gases and air, make the ensemble look like a huge lighted plum pudding. When the little jets are bashful about lighting they are encouraged to do so by a hot skimmer rod, which causes a mild running explosion and conflagration similar to that of a surly gas-oven's action after a summer's vacation.

A few minutes after the pouring is completed, the moulder, whose moulds have just been filled, has the most difficult problem of all on his hands—in fact if the condition has been a peculiar one, the foreman himself will be on the spot exercising brain and shovel. About two or three minutes after a pouring, the iron is said to be "set," but is still a wicked, glowering red which takes until the morning after to cool completely. The crane picks off the cope after the clamps have been removed and the moulder then tries his hand at estimating where the casting should be covered or weighted still more with sand, and where uncovered or "stripped." If the casting be of equal thickness throughout there is but slight danger of any certain part kicking up its heels and warping, but since such conditions occur only rarely, the moulder is generally presented with the problem of so uncovering the parts where the metal is thickest and covering those portions which are thinnest, that the forced retarded rate of cooling of thin parts will equal the greater shrinkage and naturally slower cooling of the thicker sections. Clever manipulation will bring about an almost true casting, whereas unskilled sand shovelling may result in a casting which will take hours to straighten or necessitate a new one's being poured. Some foundries prefer pursuing another policy—of allowing the casting to cool as slowly as possible without removing any sand from the heavier portions as described above. The reason is that even though not perfectly straight on cooling, a casting can be trued up easier because of slow cooling than though it had been uncovered. Thus there is always a choice of stripping the casting, hoping it will cool perfectly true (but with the chance that if it does not it will be difficult to straighten), or, to allow the iron to cool as slowly as possible, fearing that it will not likely be perfect but with the consolation that it will be more easily trued up than a more quickly cooled product. A skilled foundry can cast pilasters 25 feet long and panels 12 x 5 feet which are perfectly straight, but that can be done only by a first-class organization and expresses about the limit as to length and square

footage. As an old hand at the game will observe, almost any foundry may be able to cast a panel whose ornament will hide flaws, but it is a feat of far greater skill to be able to cast a huge plain panel without blemish or warp.

To return to the stripping of the castings: when the moulder or foreman is satisfied that the adjusted blanket of sand is about right, and that the iron can stand something of a shock, he uses a hammer or shovel to knock off the upstanding roots which formerly served as sprues and risers. When cooled these latter will serve as fodder for the insatiable cupola, and the places where they are broken off will be

FIG. 136

The foundry after pouring—the hot iron can be seen glowing in the small moulds to the right centre, while the travelling crane has picked up the cope of a large mould and has it suspended in mid-air

ground evenly on the morrow. The day is over as far as the castings are concerned, except to cool off and change from a cherry red to a gray color.

The finale for the day, when all moulds are poured and properly stripped, comes with emptying the cupola of whatever residue liquid metal cannot be drained into the exterior mixing ladle. If allowed to cool the iron would solidify and prevent re-opening at any future time. So all hands stand clear, while with a Seminole war-whoop, the master of cupola ceremonies pulls out the metal support of the two semicircular bottom doors. The golden dregs hit the floor of the foundry with a dull thud, liquid fire spatters in a thousand directions, and clouds of smoke, soot and dust swirl up to the skylights. For a brief moment the foundry glows with brilliant flood lights, but in a twinkling is enveloped by dense London pea-soup fog. The dust and soot settle, the smoke and gases clear—and the curtain is rung down for another day.

When the castings have cooled overnight they pass from the foundry to a sandblasting machine, which disperses whatever moulding sand may adhere. Large excrescences, as where there have been gates and risers, are ground or cut off. After this the course of the iron through the plant is much the same as wood would pursue in a cabinetmaker's establishment. All surfaces to be fitted are carefully sawed so as to fit exactly. In first-class operations there are no screw heads showing except in rare cases of necessity, but instead, parts are tapped to flanges on the back and drawn together with rods and bolts. Warped castings are coaxed and reformed by heating and peening (beating with rounded end of hammer). The same care and fitting are given the component parts of

the iron as would occur in wood joinery, but the handling is much more difficult of course because of the weight and ungainly size of the members. As far as refining the ornament is concerned, there is no parallel between iron and bronze, which is chased and polished. When the iron casting comes out of the mould and is bereft of clinging sand, it stands before the world as it is likely always to look, except for its coats of paint. The only remedy for surface flaws or general unsatisfactory results lies in making new castings. This should be ordered by the architect if such be necessary, for he can get quite as good an idea of the quality of his job at this time as later when erected at the building. True, parts must still be assembled and fitted, but more than likely if the castings are practically perfect, the fitting will be equally creditable. But this too should be inspected.

CHARACTERISTICS AFFECTING DESIGN

THE properties of cast iron which are of interest to the architect and designer involve not so much its chemical parentage as its physical attributes and those natural propensities which affect fabrication. The fact that cast iron differs from other brands of iron or steel by its relative carbon content (this averaging from 3 to 3.7 per cent) is not as important to the designer as the fact that when molten it does not flow as readily as bronze, and its higher melting point makes it more apt to burn the unbaked mould and thus produce a roughened surface. These two factors contribute largely to the reasons why cast iron cannot maintain the sharpness or minuteness of detail which is inherently associated with bronze casting. Accepting these traits as unalterable, the only recourse for the architect who desires to design properly for cast iron, is not to visualize his product in bronze and mentally sigh because it will be poured in iron, but to depend upon simple, dignified and well proportioned forms suggestive of strength, without intricate ornament at a fine scale. A most intelligent modern employment is by Zantzinger, Borie & Medary, architects, in their building for the Fidelity Mutual Life Insurance Company, Philadelphia, (pages 129-131), in the great arch and window spandrels. Lee Lawrie, the sculptor, so modeled the panels and ornament as to bring out the best qualities of cast iron; not only did the

models remain well within the natural limitations of iron, but the finished products cheerfully lent themselves to effective polychroming in gold leaf and deep blue. No less creditable is the "modern" mannered ornament in the window spandrels of the Home Savings Bank, Albany, New York, by Dennison & Hirons, architects (page 135). Here the same simplicity is present, which takes cognizance of cast iron as such, and makes virtue out of necessity by designing within the capabilities of unbaked sand moulds.

Since cast iron should be painted in order to be protected from atmospheric conditions, the designer does well previously to consider how the executed design will appear after it has had at least one application of red lead (or red oxide of iron) paint, followed by another covering coat. Probably every architect who has seen his plaster models in the shops, and later mentally compared them with the erected work, has lamented the loss in sharpness and refinement of detail, and consequently has either been discouraged with the material, or else comes to realize that to achieve a creditable effect both his designers and himself should more clearly understand the possibilities and limitations of the gray metal. The very fact that cast iron should be painted can become a a valuable asset instead of a liability if its rôle be properly considered in its color relation to the other building materials comprising the design ensemble. In all the other metals which "weather" and acquire a "patina" there is no good reason for the ornament to display any but the naturally acquired color, while cast iron opens up a lively array of possibilities. If the design be so worked out that even the hard-hearted owner is melted by the charm of the ornament or pattern in color, he may of his own accord be convinced that it will be a business asset to have the polychroming renewed after several years of exposure. Since repainting is usually not done under the supervision of the architect it is obviously well to have a simple scheme with but few colors and those easily mixed. The above mentioned blue and gold panels again are illustrative of wisdom aforethought.

Almost every building in some phase or another records a change in design which was brought about by being either prohibitive in cost, or by conditions which were impossible to fabricate or erect as shown on the estimate drawings. Problems in cast iron are no less complicated than for any other metal, and it bears repetition to state that greater speed is eventually obtained in the final completion of a building if in the early stages the architect invites the suggestions and criticisms of a thoroughly capable cast iron expert. It is difficult to generalize as to the deficiencies which foundries commonly find in architects' drawings. Each new building offers special conditions, but for general purposes of design some of the limitations which should be observed are as follows:

(a) Greatest length of such forms as pilasters or engaged columns, 25 feet.

(b) Greatest area of panels in single castings as spandrels, about 60 square feet, as 12 x 5 feet.

(c) General pouring thickness $\frac{5}{16}$ to $\frac{1}{2}$ inch for large castings, $\frac{1}{4}$ to $\frac{5}{16}$ inch if for small.

(d) For pierced work, as grilles, minimum section $\frac{3}{16}$ inch wide (for face exposed) and $\frac{1}{4}$ inch deep.

(e) There should be no undercutting of ornament; twisted bars should not be expected in cast iron and nothing is gained—they are very easily wrought.

Arc-welding can readily be done, as well as bolting together from the unseen rear faces to eliminate screw heads. The time involved from the date of signing the contract to the delivery and erection on the job, for any sizable operation with the usual number of trying problems, is about the same as for bronze, viz. ten to twelve weeks at an optimistic minimum, with fourteen a safer allowance. This is dependent of course upon the architect's organization supplying all details for models and working-drawing promptly, as well as checking shop-drawings immediately upon their reception.

The properties which make cast iron differ from wrought are such that as far as workability is concerned, it is another metal. Whereas wrought iron is always willing to bend to reason by coaxing with a forge fire and hammer, cast iron when once poured is absolutely "set in its ways." It may be slightly "trued up" by heat and hammer, but in no sense is it workable. It becomes so brittle that an ornamental casting if dropped is practically certain to break. The "white" cast iron (never used in architectural work) is fine grained, exceedingly brittle, and so hard it cuts like a diamond; "gray" iron is more malleable, soft and tough.

According to Ossa Sowers, New York metallurgist and practical expert in foundry practice, "cast iron is less acted upon by the moisture in the atmosphere and is less corrosive than other kinds of cheap commercial iron; it is an excellent casting material, is more rigid than other forms of iron and withstands great compression." The quality of serving structurally, and yet being ornamental, is one of the proudest assets of the material—not any of its metallic rivals can accept as much structural responsibility. For this reason when architecture in this country could but rarely afford to have the actual structural members enclosed by a costly veneer, cast iron was widely and effectively used (New Orleans examples, pages 118 and 120). Cast iron columns can be both useful and ornamental for the same money; where wood would be insufficiently permanent or strong, cast iron can be so perfectly substituted that, after the usual painting, the difference cannot be cursorily detected (page 127).

PAINTING

The painting of cast iron as insurance against the damage by moisture in the atmosphere should be of interest to the architect not only for its protective qualities, but also for preserving the creditable appearance of workmanship and design. It may easily happen that the architect designed the cast iron with irreproachable merit, that the foundry executed the work without flaw and erected it without a joint or screw head visible, and yet a painter may come along with too much paint in his brush and too little pride in his work and utterly ruin the entire effect. Nothing is more unsightly in a cast iron panel than hardened rivulets of superfluous paint, unless it be a scattering of blow holes. The worst enemy of sharp detail is not so much the "green" sand of the foundry mould, as an excessively thick coat of paint, or, what is still more common, successive generations of paint. The architect has unfortunately but little influence with the owner once the building is completed, and the latter is not likely to listen to any exhortations of the architect that before the cast iron be painted again the old paint should be burned off. Yet unquestionably this is what should be done to keep the iron looking like its pristine self. In this day of intent-on-income clients, perhaps the only weapon of the architect is vigorously to recommend that old paint be burned off before repainting because otherwise all detail will steadily disappear and actually result in a cash loss to the owner—the loss of the cost of the original ornament.

Not only should the architect give the cast iron painting his attention on the job, but also in its first initiation at the plant where it receives a coat of red lead or red oxide of iron paint. This coat can be unnecessarily heavy to the detriment of the ornament also. Instead of the fiery vermilion of the natural red lead, some good companies use a quiet gray priming which is easier to cover by a light color, thus saving an extra coat of paint and additional loss of sharpness.

In addition to cheering up cast iron by painting, there are a number of other means at the disposal of the designer. The enamelling (by fusing, not applying paint) of certain portions like so much champlevé ornament (page 181) has been used in England with excellent effect. Another possibility for interior work, in eliminating painting, is to grease the iron with a heavy oil and then heat it to a cherry red; on cooling it should be waxed. If occasional waxing or oiling is administered after installation, the natural gray color of the iron will be maintained and the maximum sharpness of the casting retained; for certain design effects this method may advantageously be employed. As regards electro-plating with another metal, electro-galvanizing or cadmium coating, these may be successfully done for interior work, as far as finish is concerned. Whether the cost expended is repaid by a more advantageous finish which will better resist corrosion, and whether the loss in sharpness of ornament due to the coating is a serious consideration, are questions open to discussion. When cast iron is intelligently painted it is almost equally well protected from the weather, loses less of its detail, and is far more inexpensive. In Paris, however, the street lamp posts are said to be satisfactorily electro-plated. There is now a German invention on the market which appears to yield excellent results; this consists of a small acetylene gun which is fed by wire, the flame melting the latter and allowing the molten metal to be sprayed on to any desired thickness. Any metal which comes in the form of wire may be used. Naturally the thicker the coat the greater the loss in detail. Still another process, which seems to be less expensive than those mentioned, and which has proved satisfactory for the last ten years, is described under "Chemical Surface Action" (page 188).

ESTIMATE DRAWINGS

All metal craftsmen, when asked the main criticism of architects' estimate drawings, reply without a moment's hesitation that these should never be less than ¾ inch to the foot, and still better 1½ inches, for details of ornament and special conditions, and that the drawings as well as the specifications should be absolutely definite, so that there is a fair opportunity for the estimator to know *exactly* what he is to figure on furnishing. Some architects who are afraid of omitting something unwittingly, in order to save checking-back at the time of issuing estimating plans and specifications, and embarrassment in case a forgotten item turns up later, insert enough ambiguous clauses of far-reaching intent in the specifications so that the contractor in effect may be held responsible to furnish almost anything which the architect deems necessary to the æsthetic success of the job. Under those conditions the client may expect estimates with wide variations: some of the contractors will "play safe" by making proper allowance for the work they will be expected to furnish which is neither drawn nor specified (but broadly hinted as existing somewhere within the realm of the architect's imagination), or they may submit a low bid in order to get the work. Indefinite drawings and specifications are a poor game at best, with all parties playing a losing hand—the client loses the amount of an "extra" which he thought should have been covered in the original contract, the contractor loses the cost of the work which he has to contribute at the "compromise" conference at the sacrifice of a part of his earned profits, and the architect loses his prestige with the client and his temper with the contractor.

FIG. 137.—CAST IRON GRILLE, DOORWAY OF THE CABILDO, NEW ORLEANS

This design was obviously intended to be cast, as exemplified by the intersecting members (forming the border of little squares) all being flush. The diminutive curves forming leaves within the squares, however, appear more wrought than cast because of their thinness

FIG. 138.—BALCONY, ST. PETER AND ROYAL
STREETS, NEW ORLEANS

The austerity of the strongly accented verticals in the architecture
is harmoniously reflected in the balcony's series of vertical bars,
yet these are agreeably relieved by the circular *motifs* with wrought
curved segments and monogram, as well as triple end-brackets

FIG. 139.—BALCONY, BAYOU AND ST. JOHN
ROAD, NEW ORLEANS

This balcony turns an unusual and not displeasing trick when
it forms the corner with a panel instead of a repetition of the
running verticals. Its designer probably foresaw the front was
too narrow to foster a central feature of a monogram or circle

Photographs of Figs. 138, 139 and 140, by Richard Koch

Photograph by George W. Johnson

FIG. 140.—CAST IRON RAILING, CHARTRES
STREET, NEW ORLEANS

The scrolls above and below the spindles are wrought,
similar to those popular in Philadelphia at this time

FIG. 141.—CAST IRON BALCONY, PINCKNEY
STREET, CHARLESTON, S. C.

Whereas modern work in iron often imitates wood, balconies
of this nature never leave one in doubt as to the material

FIG. 142.—CAST IRON RAILING, FIRST AND
CHESTNUT STREETS, NEW ORLEANS

While one may feel resentful at realism in any form of art, particularly in such a refractory material as iron, yet this example of nineteenth-century American cast iron typifies a certain period and, in a measure, exhibits possibilities of the medium

FIG. 143.—DETAIL OF GATE, OLD MORTGAGE
OFFICE, NEW ORLEANS

Obviously this is a combination of cast and wrought members, as was characteristic of a certain period of New Orleans nineteenth-century work. The prickets, circles and intersecting squares are cast, while the structural bars, scrolls and curves are wrought

Photographs on this page by Richard Koch

FIG. 144.—CAST IRON GATE, MAGAZINE STREET,
NEW ORLEANS

The lyre-like form has some extremely delicate members within it, more so, in fact, than might be expected of modern work

FIG. 145.—CAST IRON GATE, 730 ESPLANADE,
NEW ORLEANS

A combination of cast with wrought work is not always as happily accomplished as here, where their scale is approximately the same

FIG. 146.—CAST GATE, AUDUBON STREET,
NEW ORLEANS   FIG. 147.—CAST PORCH, ST. CHARLES AVENUE,
NEW ORLEANS

The intricate modeling and the small penetrations typify the possibilities of good cast iron, although
the actual design in these particular examples may not have modern application without modification

Photographs on this page by Richard Koch

FIG. 148.—PONTABLA BUILDING, NEW ORLEANS
The delicate capitals and reduced entablature are noteworthy

FIG. 149.—CAST AND WROUGHT GATE, SOUTH BATTERY, CHARLESTON, S. C.

FIG. 150.—CAST IRON RAILING, THE OCTAGON, WASHINGTON, D. C.

FIG. 151.—CAST IRON BALCONY, ART MUSEUM, SAVANNAH, GA.
A type of balcony which leaves no doubt that each and every part of it was cast

FIG. 152.—CAST IRON GATE, BRUTON CHURCH, WILLIAMSBURG, VA.

FIG. 153.—CAST IRON WITH WROUGHT SCROLLS, MOBILE, ALA.

FIG. 154.—CAST IRON BALCONY, PLANTERS' HOTEL, CHARLESTON, S. C.

FIG. 155.—CAST IRON BALCONY, PRIOLAU AND EXCHANGE EAST, CHARLESTON, S. C.

FIG. 157.—CAST IRON GATE, 36 MONTAGUE STREET, CHARLESTON, S. C.
Situated on a bleak city street this floral expression in iron might appear incongruous, but
as a part of a garden mosaic of shadows and color, it should be an enviable supplement

FIG. 156.—CAST IRON BRACKETS FOR AWNING SUPPORT, MOBILE, ALA.
While the modern awning possesses some advantages in being drawn up, supports and
all, it never succeeds in being decorative in any position as does this venerable prototype

CAST IRON: ILLUSTRATIONS

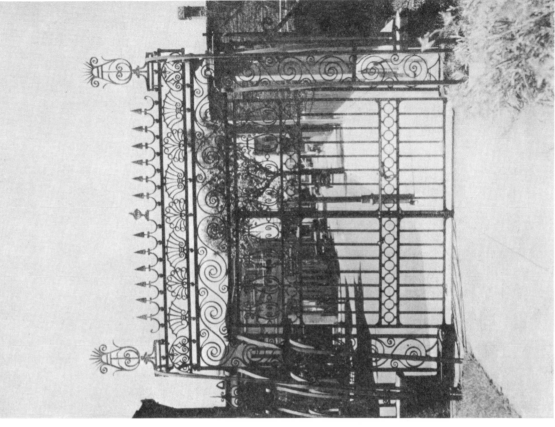

FIG. 158.—CAST IRON GATEWAY, QUEEN'S STREET, CHARLESTON, S. C.
The usual scrolls which surmount gates lack scale because of too few members; while this design can be improved upon, it proclaims the virtue of small units

FIG. 159.—CAST IRON GATES, ST. PAUL'S CHURCH, CHARLESTON, S. C.
One wonders why the wrought iron scrolls were resorted to in the side and bottom frame, when the cast frieze and cresting fulfil their mission more creditably

METAL CRAFTS IN ARCHITECTURE

Figs. 160 and 161, courtesy of Pennsylvania Museum, Memorial Hall, Philadelphia

FIG. 160 (LEFT) AND 161 (RIGHT).—CAST IRON STOVE PLATES, PENNSYLVANIA-GERMAN, 1741 AND 1749

FIG. 162.—CAST IRON BALCONY, ESTATE OF EDWARD D. BRANDEGEE, ESQ., JAMAICA PLAINS, MASS.

FIG. 163.—CAST IRON ENTRANCE PORCH AND BALCONY, JEWETT REPERTORY THEATRE, BOSTON, MASS.

J. William Beal Sons, Architects

James McKinney & Son, Craftsmen

FIG. 164.—CAST IRON WINDOW FRAME AND PANELS, INTEGRITY TRUST COMPANY BUILDING,
PHILADELPHIA

Paul Cret, Architect   Smyser-Royer Company, Craftsmen

FIG. 165.—CAST IRON WINDOWS AND SPANDRELS, FIDELITY MUTUAL LIFE INSURANCE BUILDING, PHILADELPHIA

Zantzinger, Borie & Medary, Architects   (See details on two following pages)   Smyser-Royer Company, Craftsmen

FIG. 167.—DETAIL OF FRIEZE AT BOTTOM. (2ND PANEL FROM RIGHT)
FIG. 166.—DETAIL OF WINDOW HEAD AND SPANDREL
GREAT ARCH, FIDELITY MUTUAL LIFE INSURANCE BUILDING, PHILADELPHIA
Zantzinger, Borie & Medary, Architects   Smyser-Royer Company, Craftsmen
(See previous page for general view)

CAST IRON: ILLUSTRATIONS

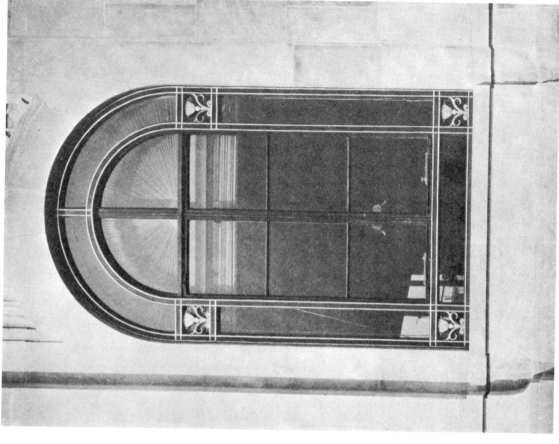

FIG. 169.—DETAIL OF FIRST FLOOR WINDOW
CAST IRON WINDOW FRAMES AND SPANDRELS, FIDELITY MUTUAL LIFE INSURANCE BUILDING, PHILADELPHIA
Zantzinger, Borie & Medary, Architects   All the iron is painted blue (appearing black in this reproduction) and gold (appearing white)   Smyser-Royer Company, Craftsmen

FIG. 168.—GROUP OF TYPICAL WINDOWS

FIG. 170.—DETAIL AT CORNER OF CAST IRON ENTRANCE GATES, JOHN WANAMAKER RESIDENCE, ELKINS PARK, PHILADELPHIA

John T. Windrim, Architect   Smyser-Royer Company, Craftsmen

This detail of pilaster cap and lamp base is illustrated as an excellent example of what lies within the possibilities of fine cast iron workmanship. Only the volutes and swags under the lamp base are "undercut," yet the effect of the *ensemble* gives the appearance of many false cores having been necessary for the casting. Plain, pierced, and ornamented surfaces are played one against the other

FIG. 171.—DETAIL OF CAST IRON PILASTER ARABESQUE AND MOULDINGS, AND PIERCED GRILLE, ELVERSON BUILDING, PHILADELPHIA

Rankin, Kellogg & Crane, Architects   Smyser-Royer Company, Craftsmen

The architect is prone to expect poor workmanship from cast iron because of repeated unfortunate results. Blow-holes in plain surfaces, untrue edges of mouldings, puttied-up ornament, uncertain and clumsy pierced work, have lessened confidence in the capabilities of the material. There is no reason, however, why cast iron cannot be as perfectly satisfactory as that illustrated here

Fig. 172.—cast iron entrance and show-window

Fig. 173.—detail at corner of top of entrance

Packard Motor Building, Philadelphia

Albert Kahn, Inc, Architect; Philip S. Tyre, Resident Architect

Smyser-Royer Company, Craftsmen

Piercing the pilaster wisely introduces the same black color as the glass presents, and thus lightens a design which might otherwise have appeared heavy and non-metallic

FIG. 174.—CAST IRON MULLIONS AND SPANDRELS, HOME SAVINGS BANK, ALBANY, N. Y.

Dennison & Hirons, Architects

James McKinney & Son, Craftsmen

The flatness of the manner *moderne* is particularly suitable to cast iron, since it does not insist upon the "undercuts" which are often essential to the "color" of Classic ornament

FIG. 175.—CAST IRON CEILING GRILLE, LIMA TRUST COMPANY, LIMA, OHIO
Weary & Alford Company, Architects   James McKinney & Son, Craftsmen
Executed in bronze this would be an admirable single-casting, but being of cast iron makes it doubly noteworthy for delicacy and perfection

FIG. 176.—CAST IRON ENTRANCE, CONSOLIDATED GAS COMPANY, NEW YORK CITY
Warren & Wetmore, Architects   James McKinney & Son, Craftsmen

FIG. 177.—CAST IRON ENTRANCE, FEDERAL TRUST BUILDING, NEWARK
Dennison & Hirons, Architects; George E. Jones, Associated Architect   James McKinney & Son, Craftsmen

FIG. 178.—ENTRANCE TRANSOM, STANDARD SAVINGS
& LOAN ASSOCIATION, UNION CO. OF DETROIT
George D. Mason & Co., Architects
Superb Bronze & Iron Co., Inc., Craftsmen

FIG. 179.—CAST IRON CEILING GRILLE, LIMA TRUST
COMPANY, LIMA, OHIO
Weary & Alford Company, Architects
James McKinney & Son, Craftsmen

FIG. 180.—EXTERIOR CAST IRON SPANDREL, JOHN HANCOCK BUILDING, BOSTON
Parker, Thomas & Rice, Architects   Smyser-Royer Company, Craftsmen

COPPER

HISTORY

U P to a century ago the term "copper" designated a different metal, in so far as general usage was concerned, from the product as we now know it, due to the presence of other elements which made it an alloy of varying characteristics. The manner of refining the ore was in no sense as thorough as at present. As late as the nineteenth century bronze formulæ specified a certain percentage of "red copper" along with another portion of "yellow," the latter probably being a form of brass with a zinc content unconsciously present. Some hinges of the Middle Ages were said to be of cast copper —if this be accurate they bear testimony to the accomplishment of a difficult task. It would seem from a variety of these and other indications that the metal known popularly as copper was actually a species of brass because of a small amount of zinc present. Also, a certain amount of tin may sometimes have produced a form of bronze. Ironically enough, although we may take pride in the uniformity and chemical purity of modern copper, there seems to have been a loss more than equal to this gain in the subtraction of certain elements which in the past have increased the longevity over the modern product. Many an architect on reading of copper relics of several thousand years ago must do so with mental reservations as he remembers either his own or some confrère's experience with it, which did not even outlive the client's wrath.

There are but rare examples of decorative copper usage which can be found, although in utilitarian rôles, such as roofs, it played an important part for centuries. Historical records indicate that copper was introduced into northern and eastern Europe from Asia. In Assyria, Egypt, Greece, Etruria, and Rome it was not used in its pure state, but during the "Gothic" period, from the twelfth through the fifteenth centuries, it was employed without alloys and frequently gilded; during this time it seems to have supplanted bronze to some extent. Portable altars were much in vogue, composed of small, flat marble slabs covered by copper plates which were chased and gilded. Two shrines survive at the Hotel Cluny from the

church of Ségry near Issoudun (Indre), from the twelfth century. One is 20½ inches long, 7 wide, and 17 high, of copper which is by turn engraved, *repoussé*, gilded and enamelled; the other is 18 inches long, 14 high, and of copper similarly decorated. In France during the thirteenth and fourteenth centuries effigies were frequently beaten from the red metal, and had parts enlivened by champlevé enamel (Figure 186). According to C. Drury E. Fortnum, "perhaps the latest of the Limoges tombs still preserved in France is that in the Louvre, the recumbent effigy of Blanche of Champagne (1283), wife of John I, Duke of Brittany. It is of beaten and gilt copper plates upon an oak core, the pillow, etc., enamelled, the head in *repoussé*." From 1100 to 1400 the Limoges artists produced "monuments, church vessels, candelabra, etc., of gilt and enamelled copper."

FIG. 181.—GREAT DRAGON OF GHENT BELFRY

Formerly this gilt copper dragon on iron framework, measuring over 12 feet from tip to tail, occupied a similar perch in Bruges. Legend places its original position on a Viking ship of the fleet of King Sigurd. It is certain that at one time it was fixed over either St. Sophia or the gate to the palace of Bucolean at Constantinople. In 1204 it was given to the returning "Brugeois" by Baldwin IX

During the troubled fourteenth century the craft declined and finally ceased, although a century later under Francis I it was resumed under different form. Until the thirteenth century the Byzantine ruled the Limoges school, but after that the Gothic held sway. In 1454 M. van Rhode created the great copper gilt figure of St. Michael (17 feet high) to surmount the spire of the Hotel de Ville, Brussels. Copper was sometimes employed for chandeliers, one of the best known being the great circle of copper gilt enamel inscriptions on the hanging lights at Hildesheim. During the Renaissance copper was used in *repoussé* vessels, utensils, high and low relief sculptures, and even for figures on a solid core. In Spain the justly admired doors to the Court of the Oranges at the Mosque of Cordoba are copper-plated over wood; these were made by the Moors after the Reconquest. Knockers were sometimes fashioned from solid copper as though of iron. In England copper frequently found itself hoisted aloft in weather-vanes, the oldest being at Etchingham; it dates from the latter part of the fourteenth century, and is composed of a banner of arms in pierced copper. The famous Brandenburg Gate of Berlin is surmounted by a copper chariot, four horses and a winged Victory; Napoleon took them to Paris in 1807 but seven years later they were replaced Unter den Linden, apparently no worse for age or travelling. In the United States we have no equally ancient copper statuary, although a good example of such usage is the quadriga of the State Capitol at St. Paul, Minnesota, (Cass Gilbert, architect; Daniel Chester French and E. C. Porter, sculptors; Theo. E. Hergert, Inc. craftsmen).

METALLIC PROPERTIES AND ARCHITECTURAL USAGES

COPPER has well merited its popularity in architectural employment for both ease in working and permanency. Its chief physical properties are malleability, ductility and facility in forming. Because of its relative softness it is one of the least expensive building materials to work by hand. Scarcely another metal combines low cost and permanency, with lightness, strength, desirable color before and after exposure, and versatility in both practical and ornamental usages. For statuary on buildings at a fair distance above the eye level, copper serves almost as well as bronze in appearance, yet costs and weighs only a fraction as much; if properly made it will last as long. Its lightness and free-from-upkeep qualities make it suitable for simple or enriched cornices, for crestings or panels which can be stamped at a reasonable cost, and its accommodating nature admits of easy erection. Parts may be united by soldering or welding, both of which can be done in such a workmanlike manner as to be unnoticeable a few feet distant, and then only when new; brief exposure soon obliterates the joints. After once erected, particularly outside, the oxidation of the air administers a beautiful green patina which is only skin-deep but which prevents further inroads of atmospheric damage. The color is not only a decided artistic asset but possesses the happy virtue of rendering unnecessary any further attention to the copper.

Copper seems best utilized when sculptural and simple architectural forms are made from it to be placed above the eye level, rather than the attempt to fashion it into small pilasters as for show-window fronts, where the corners will not be as scrupulously sharp as if cast, and where the natural green patina is likely to be supplanted by uncouth black tarnish from the human elbowing it receives. Entablatures, spandrels, crestings, building statuary, etc., are genially and happily served. For interior work only occasionally are its possibilities plumbed and never to the full depths: ornamental coffers can intelligently interpret intricate Renaissance versions, skylights can be enriched by pierced patterns or be set off by rhapsodies in relief decoration, pierced and silhouette possibilities may be combined with soffits, friezes, or other sources of illumination. The new development of depositing copper

FIG. 182.—COPPER ROOF, BASEL CATHEDRAL

This Swiss cathedral, originally dedicated in 1019, but largely rebuilt after a disastrous earthquake in 1356, has a copper roof with a green and yellow pattern

on glass is considered under "Current Developments" (page 186), and lead-coated copper under "Lead" (page 158).

Copper sheets are designated according to the weight in ounces per square foot, while bronze is spoken of in terms of "gauge"; 24-ounce copper is about the same thickness as 20-gauge bronze. Forty-eight-ounce copper (used in making statuary) is about $\frac{1}{16}$-inch thick; 24-ounce is about $\frac{1}{32}$ or .0324 inches.

MODERN METHODS OF WORKING COPPER

ARCHITECTURAL copper is seldom, if ever, cast, but is formed either by stamped, *repoussé* or spun work. Each of these methods applies to different types of work, and while the craftsmen who excell in one are likely to consider other ways of working the metal as being competitive, to the architect it seems at once evident that one means of working is more applicable to one class of work than to another.

Stamping is a mechanical means by which sheets of copper (4 by 3 feet at a maximum for each sheet) may be bent up or ornamented. It is therefore particularly useful for entablatures, pilaster caps, statuary groups which are to duplicate plaster models, and in repeating *motifs*, as spandrel panels. Assuming that the architect has approved plaster of Paris models and that these have been received by the copper craftsman, the first business in hand is to cast two dies for each section of copper to be stamped. One would be the exact replica and the other the reverse, so that when they are accurately placed in a stamping machine, one above the copper sheet and the other directly below it, on coming together (*i. e.* the upper part dropping with great force on the lower), the copper would receive its first impression of the future form it is to take. The upper die comes down as a hammer several times, each blow making the indentations deeper and more nearly approaching the original model. After a few blows the copper is annealed (heated and allowed to cool slowly) so that it will not be brittle but, on the contrary, more receptive to the further action of the die. Copper can be annealed six or seven times, and if three blows are struck between each heating, the resulting twenty operations produce a close approximation of the approved model. Naturally the stamped copper cannot be quite as sharp as the original plaster, but it comes very close to it in an expert's shop. Proper attention should be paid by the architect when he sees the model, first in clay and then in plaster, to make the detail sharper than he wishes the copper

eventually to be, or the erected work will be a disappointment.

The process of inserting a sheet of copper between two dies and letting one drop on the other sounds simple enough, but the stamping art is one beset by many difficulties. First is the preparation of the zinc dies and the care

Courtesy of Metropolitan Museum of Art

Fig. 183.—Part of a Copper Repoussé Crown
(french, fourteenth century)

essential to the casting of perfect replicas without damage to the plaster models, so that as the die wears down or for other reasons must be replaced, new ones can be made. After the dies have served their purpose the zinc can be re-melted and used again, but for each such repetition the loss in metal is from 6 to 10 per cent. The casting of the dies is in the regular foundry manner, not unlike that for the casting of bronze as described previously (pages 21–27). When the dies are completed the nicety of their adjustment in the stamping machine is no child's play, for should the upper descend out of alignment, not only would the copper be useless, but the dies themselves would be ruined and require replacing. The actual stamping, in regulating the rise and fall of the top die or hammer, requires the most unfaltering attention, for one false move ruins the stamper's hand for life. Every shop has workmen with

FIG. 184.—WEATHER-VANE FROM SANDY HILL CHURCH, AMESBURY, MASSACHUSETTS. (1715)

maimed hands as mute evidence of the dangers resultant from a moment's forgetfulness.

It is self-evident that, in the stamping of a single sheet of copper, there cannot be any undercuts. These must be obtained in another manner, and while they can be accomplished on a fair scale, it is impossible to secure them for minute modeling. If, for example, an acanthus leaf were to be curved at its termination, this would be done by stamping out the top of the leaf from one piece of copper and the bottom of the leaf from another sheet, and then either soldering or welding them together along the sides. For work above the eye level or where it would not be readily seen, the edges to be joined are carefully fitted as a butt joint and then soldered from the back; any superfluity of solder which might seep through would be scraped off after cooling. The more nearly perfect juncture is made by welding the two pieces together, playing a torch on the back faces (after they have been carefully fitted so that they meet exactly), and then melting some additional copper into the seam. This can be done so expertly that the joint is scarcely visible a few feet distant.

For another class of copper work in which the craftsman is given not a model but the architect's sketch or perspective of a head, grotesque, or special ornament which is not to be repeated, the *repoussé* method is preferably employed. By this process the copper can be humored and sufficiently "drawn" or beaten out so that an entire head with undercuts may be executed from a single sheet. First the copper is beaten out from the back until it has

assumed the general form desired. It is then placed on a pitch block and a gas flame played upon it until the pitch fills up all the spaces behind the copper. With this resilient backing the craftsman is at liberty to begin the modeling on the front face of the copper by means of punches, round, flat and otherwise, being gently tapped with a hammer or mallet. As the modeling progresses, or in undercut work, it frequently becomes necessary to remove the copper from the pitch and fit it in another position. Annealing must occasionally be done, of course, while the beating is in progress.

Where there is to be only one modeled unit it is likely to be cheapest to take a sketch to an able craftsman and have him fashion the copper by the *repoussé* method; while if there were to be a number of similarly ornamented panels or a running band of enrichment, the simpler proceeding would consist in having the unit first modeled in plaster and the copper stamped. The two processes are for different types of work and each can be equally craftsmanlike and creditable in appearance.

Another class of copper work is fashioned by the so-called spun method. The field in which this would be used is characterized by many circular lighting-bowls. It is done by forcing a sheet of copper to conform gradually to a revolving wood block by varying the pressure and position of a wood tool or chuck. If the bowl were to have a flat bottom the copper would retain the original thickness there, but as the copper sheet is forced to bend up to form the sides it would become decreasingly thinner. There is but little architectural employment for spun work in the building itself, but an extensive field exists in lighting fixtures and other adjuncts which are circular in section through parallel planes. Copper less than 24-gauge is not used, except where there is but little "spinning" to be done, because of the diminishing thickness.

The copper craft is a decidedly limited one in point of numbers. The best artisans, as for other metals, have come from Europe, where their apprenticeship has been long and thorough. The decreasing immigration since the World War has begun to make itself felt and should prompt us to stimulate an interest in the craft. It will be a difficult task, of course, to inculcate the love of pure endeavor in youth which has been brought up in an atmosphere of quantity production with high wages from the start.

DESIGN LIMITATIONS AND SHOP PRACTICE

THERE is not much to cramp the designer's desires in copper if he translate at a coarser scale whatever he would do in bronze. Pierced ornament cannot have the *finesse* of cast detail but may effectively serve as a simple silhouette; crestings, if small, can be in heavy relief but without undercuts except on a large scale; pilasters cannot be expected to have overly sharp edges and are not particularly suited to the material; entablatures are well within the realm of stamped copper and are capable of great variety. Sculptural groups have often been planned for bronze but finally made from copper with excellent results.

In both stamping or *repoussé* the more the copper is worked the thinner it becomes; in fact it will suffer a reduction of about one-third before becoming irritable to the point of cracking. Because of this the architect should realize that in order to erect a cornice of not less than 16-ounce copper and preferably 18 or 20, the copper must start out considerably thicker. The allowance which must be made for the diminution in section is dependent upon the depth of the draw; this a good craftsman can closely estimate, if given the sum of the greatest projections on both sides of the line taken through the extremities of the profile in question. Roughly speaking, for a draw of 2 inches it would be necessary to start with 24-ounce copper in order to finish with at least 18. A large egg-and-dart stamped by a New York craftsman has a draw of 4½ inches, probably one of the deepest ever made. Sawed-out designs are usually worked from ¼-inch sheets. Small cornices might be of 16- or 20-ounce copper, but any generous sized one should be at least 24; shortsighted economy is usually the most expensive item in a building.

When economy is an important factor in a design, the architect can save himself considerable time and irritation if he will consult with a good craftsman before detailing at larger than ¼-inch scale. Without undue harm in the appearance some distance above the eye level, there are certain shapes which can readily be formed or supplied which may serve his purpose as adequately as a profile he might originate. It is probably not without good cause that many metal artisans complain that architects have a habit of insisting on some trivial revision from stock forms when the subject in question is located where none but the sparrows will ever appreciate its refinement. Not that metal workers object to making what they are paid for, but often they fear that if the actual cost of the operation is charged, it will raise the price so high that the client will decide not to have the work done. Most of the stampers in and around New York have been in business so long that they have assimilated a large number of templates from the best offices and from some of the best buildings erected in the East, so that it is nothing less than an advantage for the architect to consult with a shop before beginning his detailing, to determine how he may best remain within the natural limitations at the command of the craftsmen, or be readily supplied with a form previously made.

It goes without saying that if sheet copper is to be ornamented it should be done by having the relief an integral part, either stamped or beaten out by the *repoussé* method, and not merely soldered in place. The unhappy day when the applied ornament will drop off is always an imminent possibility. Occasionally there may be an exception requiring surface application, but only rarely.

Leader bands which secure the down-spout

Cliché L. P.

FIG. 185.—GILT REPOUSSÉ COPPER, IN THE SALON D'HERCULE, LE MUSÉE, VERSAILLES

to the wall will serve their purpose most adequately when they are of some heavy, durable material like bronze, which can be bolted to the wall with full assurance that they are there to stay. The deficiency of stamped copper bands soldered in place is that ice, expansion and contraction may combine sooner or later to force them off. Bronze bands may be simple, yet display thoughtful design in such a way as to be practical, inexpensive and decorative.

The best policy in regard to leader bands, in making them bronze certainties, applies as well to gutter hangers. These should serve not only the purpose of holding the gutter in place for good and all, but break up the monotony of the even bead line by some projecting curve which will infuse the interest characteristic of European precedents. For the safe support of ladders when roofs are mended, etc., hangers are advisedly spaced about 30 inches on centres. Gutter beads should be reinforced by brass cores, either by a rod of ⅜-inch diameter, or a brass bar 1 by 3/16 inch, dependent of course upon the shape of the bead. Bracing may be done with copper tubing for certain purposes. Again it bears repeating that no form of iron or steel, particularly when galvanized, should ever be used in connection with copper. It is unnecessary to mention, of course, that all nails, bolts, screws, and other supplementary parts should also be of brass or bronze.

Because of the ease in forming copper, less time is necessary in fabrication than for the other metals, yet for intricate work or statuary two months at least should be allowed in working out the time schedule on a building operation. Straight cornice work, involving only bending the sheets into profiles, will of course take considerably less time, but it may so happen that the shops have already contracted for their capacity output for a time. In the event of great speed being necessary, the architect can determine the time allowance only by consulting various craftsmen. In the average building operation, if the copper shop be given the details two months before the work is needed, it should generally be a sufficient margin.

In order to make the drawings and specifications complete so as to obtain definite estimates, there is perhaps less labor for the architect's organization than for any of the other metals. Points that should be clearly marked, however, are: the thickness of sheet to be used; full-size profiles, so that the amount of draw can accurately be figured; typical ornamentation and conditions at intersections, shown at ¾-inch scale at least; all structural and reinforcing members marked to be copper tubing, brass or bronze; all screws, nails, bolts, etc., also brass or bronze; whether or not crestings, or other freestanding features, are to be single or double faced, and if double whether the back is to be plain.

For certain purposes copper requires no care, and for others most expert attention. Wherever it is above the eye level on the exterior, or where human contact will not disturb the acquisition of its usual becoming green patina, the less done to copper the better. If, on the other hand, it be desirable to keep it bright, as for shop fronts or ornamentation where it is supposed to fill the rôle of bronze, then it may be either left in its natural state and kept polished (a difficult task) by the regular application of alkaline solutions with much elbow grease, or it may be regularly lacquered and conditioned by experts only. Before re-lacquering the remains of the old finish should be removed and the copper polished.

Copper may be induced to turn a multitude of colors and shades, but this is more particularly a specialized job to be intrusted only to an experienced artisan. Craftsmen are generally loath to divulge how certain effects are obtained, although solutions producing a number of colors (as brown, reddish bronze, blue black, antique green oxidized and verde antique) are prescribed in the booklet, "Coloring Copper and Brass," issued by the Copper and Brass Research Association, 25 Broadway, New York City. This organization has published, from time to time, valuable and extensive data on a wide range of roofing and flashing problems, including standard specifications and recommended practice for installing sheet copper work in various forms. It has a great amount of information available on this subject, as well as other applications of copper, brass and bronze in building construction. Its Building Service Department invites inquiries of any nature in problems pertaining to architectural copper, brass and bronze. The Association was organized to promote better understanding and wider usage of copper and its alloys, and gives its consulting services gratis; since its research is conducted with the view to determining the best solutions, unprejudiced in any way whatsoever, architects are referred to it for all practical problems.

FIG. 186.—RELIQUARY, OF GILT COPPER AND CHAMPLEVÉ ENAMEL. (LIMOGES SCHOOL)

FIG. 187.—COPPER GILT PLAQUE, FIGURE OF A SAINT. (FRENCH, 1150–1200)

FIG. 188.—COPPER ANDIRON, ONE OF A PAIR. (FRENCH, LATE SIXTEENTH CENTURY)

All illustrations on this page by courtesy of Metropolitan Museum of Art

FIG. 189.—COPPER GILT HINGE WITH SAINTS. (FRENCH, THIRTEENTH OR FOURTEENTH CENTURY)

FIG. 191 (ABOVE) AND FIG. 192 (BELOW).—COPPER
ROOF ORNAMENTATION, GRACE NICHOLSON ORIENTAL
ART GALLERIES, PASADENA, CAL.
Van Pelt & Maybury, Architects

FIG. 190.—STAMPED
COPPER FIGURE
Theo. E. Hergert, Inc.,
Craftsmen

FIG. 193.—STAMPED
COPPER DOLPHIN
Theo. E. Hergert, Inc.,
Craftsmen

FIG. 194.—HOLY VESSEL OR FONT OF COPPER FROM BOGOTA, COLOMBIA. (BY P. LOPEZ OF QUIROGA, 1600)

FIG. 195.—SYRIAN OR MESOPOTAMIAN BRASS INLAID WITH SILVER AND COPPER. (EARLY 14TH CENTURY)

FIG. 196.—AMERICAN-COLONIAL COPPER LEADER HEAD
The ribbed quality of the monograph letters is noteworthy, as well as the *8* and *5*

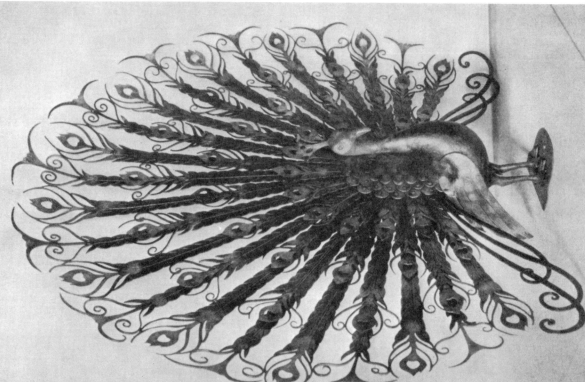

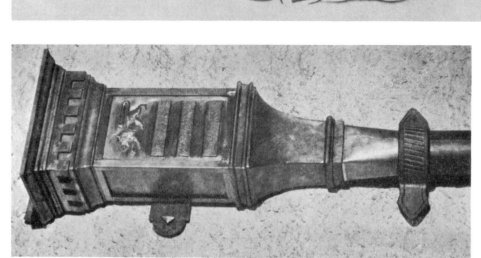

METAL CRAFTS IN ARCHITECTURE

148

Fig. 198 (left).—Wrought Copper Peacock (42 inches high) on Pergola of Residence for Mr. W. S. Farish, Houston, Texas

H. T. Lindeberg, Architect
Executed by The Iron-Craftsmen

Fig. 197 (above) and Fig. 199 (extreme right).—Copper Leader Heads, Residence of Charles Scribner, Jr., Esq., Far Hills, N. J.

Hyde & Shephard, Architects
Klein & Kavanagh, Craftsmen

LEAD: HISTORY

THE family tree of lead takes root almost as deeply in antiquity as the other metals used in the fabric and ornamentation of buildings. It comes in for Biblical reference by Ezekiel when he rebukes Phœnician merchants for a too prosperous lead and tin trade with Tarshish. In the Egyptian Museum of Berlin there is a statuette of a small girl dated 1600 B.C., and in the same collection a sensitively modeled figure of a seated boy of about 600 B.C.; both are of lead. Throughout the Mediterranean countries lead statuary has been found. The metal was often used in anchoring the clamps which bound stone courses together, by the Babylonians and Assyrians, and later by the Greeks, and initiated what in modern practice is supplanted by lead fibre or "wool," and oakum. The metal was appreciated for its malleability and low fusing point, and as a result found varying employments from Babylon to Rome in ancient history. In the pre-Christian era it invaded the field of dentistry, first by way of filling teeth previous to their extraction so as to solidify them, and later as permanent fillings. As far back as the sixth century B.C. in Sparta small images of favorite gods or goddesses were cast from it, to be either left as votive offerings at a shrine or buried with the dead. This practice of forming tokens or mementos to be carried by pilgrims continued through the mediæval period; quantities have been found along the Thames and Seine, sometimes as medals and, at other times, as tiny flasks containing revered remains. It was the Roman, however, who used lead most extensively because of the practical use to which he put it. The limited supply naturally curtailed its employment, but with the discovery of deposits in England, extensive piping systems and aqueduct linings were made of lead. At Chester, England, a chance excavation yielded up a consignment of pig lead dated 79 A.D., evidently intended to be sent back to Italy. A personal rather than architectural use was in the Roman-British coffins which have been found; some of these are ornamented with a crude design of bead and reed, appar-

ently made by pressing turned wooden rods into the sand bed before the sheet of lead was cast. Ossuaries (containers for bones) were also of lead. Although the Roman-British practice of using lead coffins died out, it was revived toward the middle of the twelfth century and continued until late in the seventeenth. Heart caskets were fashioned of lead and did service for one no less than Richard Cœur de Lion. The gray metal was also used for enclosing the articles buried with the dead.

Although ancient employment of lead may have been more architectural than the usages enumerated above, existing remains are not sufficiently intact to trace other expressions. Not until the sixth century does lead assume a definite and traceable rôle architecturally. Lethaby advances the opinion that "sheathing buildings with decorative plates of metal has been one of man's architectural instincts," and in substantiation quotes from Viollet-le-Duc: "Under the Merovingian kings (c. 500 to 752, the first Frankish dynasty in Gaul) they covered entire edifices, churches or palaces with lead. St. Eloy (also "Eloi") is said to have covered the church of St. Paul des Champs with sheets of lead artistically wrought." In Constantinople lead was used otherwise, by being laid directly over the brick domes which sprang up like mushrooms in the reign of Justinian. Laying the lead directly over the masonry domes, instead of over timber framework as was characteristic in the northern parts of Europe, naturally gave them irregular profiles; an interesting comparison may be made of a wide variety of effects and curves on the many domes of St. Sophia, which of course is the outstanding example of early lead roofing. In the East mosques and bazaars, with their characteristic series of rows of small domes, followed suit on a lesser scale. Mediæval lead became closely affiliated with architectural expression in roofs, spires, lanterns, parapets, leader heads, down-spouts, gutters, and various ornamental details. Because of the generous deposits in England it was used there earlier and more extensively than elsewhere in Europe.

FRENCH LEAD WORK

Lead played a fairly important architectural rôle in France from the fifteenth century until the end of the Empire period. Sarcophagi and monuments of the fifteenth century were frequently embellished with it; at this period Dijon had a school of lead sculptors. Lead figures were used as culminating points on church roofs, usually being *repoussé* sheets formed over wood. Weather-vanes also were fashioned from it, sometimes being enlivened by little bells swinging against a metal bowl. The lead finial became an accepted feature, and by the time of the Renaissance ornamental lead ridges on roofs were not uncommon. Some of the best known examples of the lead flèche are at St. Chapelle du Palais, Paris; transept of Notre Dame, Paris, by Viollet-le-Duc; Cathedral of Amiens; and St. Jean-du-Doigt (Finistère). The domes of the Eglise du Val-de-Grâce and the Sorbonne, Paris, are of lead, as are the towers and domes of the Château de Serrant (Maine-et-Loire). A particularly interesting steeple at Châlons-sur-Marne has faint indications of a gorgeous color scheme still remaining. Finials, crockets and *lucarne* embellishments were frequently of lead, as illustrated by the Tour de la Grosse Horloge, Rouen, the Château d'Azay-le-Rideau, the ancient Château de Gien, the house of Jacques Cœur at Bourges, and the hospital of Beaune.

The high point in French lead work was attained in the reign of *Le Grand Monarch* (Louis XIV), as exemplified by the diversified and admirable garden sculptures at Versailles. That it could be quickly cast, was much cheaper than bronze and yet would endure as well, were some of the chief factors in its favor. The most

famous sculptors of the day were employed in the modeling, and great care was exercised in accurate casting. Very properly it was not modeled in the manner of any of the other metals. It was considered essential that the artist know the traits peculiar to his material, and as a result lead work reflects an appreciation of the soft malleable quality along with "its character of gentleness and unobtrusiveness." In the magnificent gardens of Versailles, Le Nôtre employed lead extensively. It is always particularly appropriate for gardens because of its whitish patina blending harmoniously with planting, and its virtues are no better displayed than here. Precise detail was not desired as much as were appropriate silhouettes which accented the proper axes of vistas. Vases and figures lent the necessary formal contours and emphasis without distracting color and detail. At first all the lead work was gilded, but it has now weathered to a natural silvery patina; the group of the chariot of Apollo at the foot of the *tapis vert* is an especially happy example.

The usage of lead in the interior of Versailles is mentioned under "Architectural Usage and Design," (page 155), where it served as a gilt substitute for applied bronze ornament. During the Empire period it was similarly employed for decoration, being cast with great sharpness and delicacy.

In Germany lead was less commonly used, and while there are statues, statuettes, clocks, lighting fixtures, etc., made from it, they are cast less sharply than in the Empire manner of France.

FIG. 200.—PORTION OF CAST LEAD FRONT TO CISTERN, ORTHOPÆDIC HOSPITAL, LONDON. (DATE OF "1719" CAN BE SEEN)

ENGLISH LEAD WORK

Although the commercial output of lead in England has not compared with other European countries, as Spain and Germany, artistic expression in the metal has found far greater favor in her architecture and gardens than in any other country. She alone has used lead leader heads, an outgrowth of the early Roman practice of utilizing the metal for piping. While other countries have had leaden domes, roofs, steeples, statues, urns, and coffins, England has enjoyed a wider and greater range of them; cisterns, fonts and receptacles have been fashioned of lead since her mediæval days.

Just as the crockets, finials and leaf work of the crestings of French roofs have no parallel in other countries, in the same way England is unique in her employment of leader heads. The earliest period of these dates from about the middle of the fifteenth century to the middle of the sixteenth. The artisans (termed "plumbers" from the Latin word *plumbum* for lead) were a conservative set, and usually seemed to have trailed about a half century behind the design current in other mediums. The use of lead pipes for roofing purposes had earlier inception, not so much to protect pedestrians from dripping eaves as to preserve the water by conducting it to cisterns. It is of interest that in 1241 Henry III, with a thrifty turn of mind, sent a memorandum to the keeper of the works at the Tower, to the effect that, "We command you to . . . cause all leaden gutters of the great tower through which the rain water should fall from the summit of the same tower to be carried to the ground, so that the wall of the said tower, which has been newly whitewashed, may be in no wise injured by the dropping of the rain water nor be easily weakened." From the practice of fixing down-spout pipes against a wall, the need for the swelling at the top of the pipe was soon realized in order to prevent the water from overflowing the gutter; it was but a step from these practical requirements to the ornamented leader head. When down-spouts were not used the water was conducted through projecting stone gargoyles by lead troughs. Concerning downspouts, it is of interest to note Viollet-le-Duc's sage observation concerning the desirability of square or rectangular pipes compared to circular ones, because the latter cannot expand as water freezes.

Lead ornament began to show the influences of the Renaissance only in a transitional form from about the middle of the sixteenth century until the seventeenth. Design characteristics of the new movement were adopted spasmodically and provincially. Earlier heads had evinced greater wealth of invention, appreciation of the material, fondness for facial caricatures, and employment of historical symbols. The form of present-day hanging or built-in gutters was unknown before about 1600, the common type having the bottom of the gutter on the top of the wall. The outer face of gutters invited vine ornamentation. Painting and gilding were usual, as well as tinning certain parts. The chief forms used for leader head decoration were pierced lace-like designs applied flat, pierced panels forming false fronts, and pierced or solid turrets. Plain surfaces were frequently embellished by checker and chevron ornament. Due to the continuous building of Haddon Hall from 1580 to 1696, its leader heads are among the best examples of this transitional period, having outer fronts of pierced tracery which combined Gothic traits with the newer ideas of delicate cornices. Sevenoaks, Knole Park, has a series of delicately designed heads (formed between 1604-'07), and, while highly decorated like other work of the period, the ornament is wisely restrained.

After the beginning of the seventeenth century leader heads became less interesting. The architect played a more important rôle by dictating designs, and as has happened in all metal crafts at all times when such has been the case, the natural qualities of the material were lost sight of. Architects were but slightly interested in lead details. Gothic traits disappeared entirely as classical ornament and design were substituted. Mechanical skill took precedence over beauty in design, as is exhibited by impoverished lead ornamentation in even Wren's churches. The methods of casting the leader head as a sheet—bending it up in shape and soldering the seams together, or in casting the gutters in lengths out flat, bending them in shape, and soldering them together or on to the leader head—were above reproach. Dentils and other ornamentation, instead of being cast as part of the background, however, sometimes were apt to be applied with solder without even having pins driven through to the back.

Leaded spires and domes have long played an important part in English architectural history and skyline. While they were favorites of Wren (1632–1723), the roofing popularity of lead began in the thirteenth century. Concerning lead as a roofing material, Wren wrote in 1708: "Lead is certainly the best and lightest covering, and being of our own growth and manufacture, and lasting if properly laid, for many hundreds of years, is without question the most preferable." Sir Christopher may have forgotten about the existence of copper at the moment when he made the rather overenthusiastic statement, the unfortunate propensity of lead to "creep" (*i. e.* expand with heat but never contract), and the likelihood of its melting in case of fire. However, where well laid and where unscathed by fire, it must be granted that the roofing effects possible in lead are none other than artistic achievements. The finest of old English spires still existing is of thirteenth-century origin at Long Sutton, Lincolnshire. In the same century all three towers of Lincoln Cathedral were given lead spires; a "tempest" destroyed the central one in 1548, while the other two were later taken down, parsimoniously to save the expense of repairs and upkeep. Old St. Paul's once had the highest lead steeple in the world, completed in 1221; it was struck by lightning in 1561, just a century before the Fire. Lead was such a favorite of Wren's that out of twenty-eight towers he crowned all but eight with lead laid over timber construction. Many English spires have patterns and designs formed by their rolled seams, but Wren seemed content with the contrast of the lower stone or brick tower with the metal spire or cupola. When Wren used lead for the dome of St. Paul's, he was but following such precedent as St. Sophia, San Michele in Montefiascone, several in Rome, and St. Maria della Salute in Venice. It is singular that, whereas in the English countryside stone weathers dark and lead becomes silvery, just the reverse is true in London, for the stone where exposed is often almost white and the lead fairly dark. In Edinburgh there seemed to be no distinct plumbing craft during the sixteenth and seventeenth centuries, the work being done by carpenters and masons. Only one lead spire exists, that of St. Mary Magdalen; this was the church of the Hammermen, the guild to which the plumbers belonged in the seventeenth century. The method of securing the lead in place was usually to nail the sheets at the top and clip them at the bottom; the reason for the rolled joints was to allow for the expansion of the lead from the heat of the sun.

One of the earliest uses for lead in England, as well as one of the first lead forms to be decorated, were the baptismal fonts of the twelfth century. Unfortunately they have become almost a rarity because they were readily melted down for bullets, were easily accessible, and could be dispensed with. The Puritans did worse than frown with displeasure upon them because of figure decoration.

Cisterns in England cannot be traced earlier than the sixteenth century. The hue and cry of the nineteenth century against lead poisoning was responsible for the destruction of many, yet sufficient remain, particularly in London, to be of inspiration for the modern designer. The surface to be decorated was simple in form because the cistern was straight vertically and either circular or rectangular in plan; the ornament of the sides needed to be relatively flat in order that colliding buckets should not ruin projecting parts. The scheme of ornamentation was largely a matter of uniting circles and straight lines in all manner of combinations to compose a pattern of the ribs. The panels themselves were varied by the spotting of small, diversified ornaments; friezes sometimes had modeled decoration; and an all-over diapered or other unobtrusive pattern like the background of the mediæval artisan was effectively used at times, but generally seemed a forgotten possibility. London plumbers had a penchant for using stiff little figures, stars and shells; western England used more fanciful forms. Some cisterns have survived as fountain bases. Pump heads, in this same category, were sometimes of lead, but the designs on the whole were not imaginative.

The oppression of the Netherlands by Spain and the coming of many craftsmen with William of Orange to England, had its effect upon English lead work and upon the introduction of water features in gardens. The Dutch idea that the pools and fountains of a garden are its soul, took firm root in England, and while for a time the gardens of the Netherlands and France were copied, soon these became acclimatized and developed national traits of their own. As a result lead vases, fountains and figures for gardens received a tremendous impetus. As garden decoration the soft and simple modeling of lead and its silvery gray patina are of course unsurpassed.

Urns of lead were also introduced, most

successful in design when they were of solemn demeanor and placed in dignified positions. Some had suggestions of incinerary flames in the modeling of their tops, while others provided space for the growing of flowers. Decoration was frequently copied from Greek urns depicting classical myths. Other uses for lead of lesser importance were in ventilating grilles, one or two for a window, and in eighteenth-century fanlights, which were often glazed with lead, forming intricate designs enriched with rosettes and other decorative forms.

While the cheapness of casting lead figures instead of bronze ones accounts in a measure for their large numbers, it is scarcely to be regretted that so many were of the humbler metal in view of the excellence of their craftsmanship and the harmonious blending of the patina with their environment. In mediæval France the accepted manner of fashioning figures was to carve the approximate form from wood, overlay it with sheets of lead, refine the modeling by beating, and then overlap or solder the joints. This method results in ample strength without undue weight, but was never in favor in England. Here on the other hand the lead statues seem invariably to have been cast, by the *cire perdue* process if there were to be only one, and by using casting patterns or cores if there were to be a num er of reproductions. Whereas there is no foundry difficulty in substituting lead for bronze in most figures, since it casts with great precision, for large work, such as equestrian statues, it is likely to be unsatisfactory because of the weight of the material causing unsupported parts to be susceptible to sagging. An exception to this is the equestrian statue of Charles II in Parliament Square, Edinburgh. The earliest statue which can be given a date in England is the blackamoor standing at the head of the staircase holding candles in Sir Slingsby's Red House, Marston Moor; it was cast in 1638 by Andrew Karne, a Dutchman or German. Henry VIII was fond of lead, and in his reign candelabra in the form of figures were made from it. The "Neptune" in Bristol dates to Elizabeth's reign, and, according to tradition, was cast from lead pumps captured from the Armada. From William III through the reigns of the Georges, lead portraits were the popular vogue. The statue of William III in Dublin receives a coat of paint each year in order to imitate bronze, except for a few small patches which are gilded. Statues were sometimes painted in the attempt

to lend a realistic appearance, a notable example being a figure of Sir John Cass by Roubillac (completed 1751). Garden figures were frequently painted, or sometimes planted in the lawns to produce a theatrical effect. Although the majority of lead statues were of the Georgian period, the practice of casting them was well established during the seventeenth century. Eighteenth-century lead statues show impersonations of classic figures, frequently inaccurate and nondescript. Costumes were inclined to be confused and mixed. Often they possessed a Dutch air because of being modeled by Lowland sculptors who had emigrated to England.

The most important production of lead statues in England was due to John Van Nost, a Hollander who came over with William III, and set up lead works in Piccadilly. Although he carried many stock patterns, he made any number of special orders by the *cire perdue* process. While there were some monstrosities produced, such as life-sized cows, he himself was an artist of note whose influence made itself strongly felt. Some of his works suggest the characteristics of such Italian sculptors as Verrocchio. After his death in 1739 John Cheere took over the lead works, yet, as he was primarily a foundryman and but little interested in the artistic phase, he was satisfied to continue using the patterns Van Nost had left. His death in 1787 marks the end of the great lead works, none of equal importance having since existed.

(NOTE.—For a complete history of English lead, see "English Leadwork" by Sir Lawrence Weaver.)

FIG. 201—CAST LEAD FONT
The Birmingham Guild, Ltd., Craftsmen

LEAD: CRAFTSMANSHIP

CHARACTERISTICS

BECAUSE of its longevity and accommodating nature lead has been an important architectural adjunct since mediæval times. The only deteriorating agent, and that fortunately confined to relatively small areas, is a lead-hungry type of beetle-borer which may play unpleasant pranks by indulging its favorite appetite for telephone cables or fuses where lead-coated. Otherwise lead has a gilt-edge reputation which should long continue its affiliation with architecture. Its rating for dependability and usefulness may be traced in the archives of Assyria, Egypt and Sparta. More recent Roman relics date back for 1800 years or more; lead pipes and utensils, used by the victorious cohorts and excavated in England, are found to be still in good condition. The permanency of lead has ever been one of its best recommendations, regardless of in what high or lowly state of land, air or water it found itself.

While lead is such a yielding metal that it can be dented with a finger nail, it is stern morally, being pure to the extent of 99.44 per cent. However, without physical resistance it welcomes being rolled or cast into sheets, forced through a die, or bent in a wide variety of forms, without becoming brittle. Lead casts with greater delicacy than any other metal, so much so that Cellini suggested that it be used for "proofs" in gold or medalist work. Ordinary air does not corrode it, and even sulphuric acid is nonplussed. It turns the trick on oxygen by playing with it only enough to slyly form a suboxide (gray "tarnish"), and later a carbonate which looks white and acts

as an eternal insurance against further assaults of oxidation. This patina covering, while only of infinitesimal thickness, is all-sufficient protection against atmospheric corrosion, and if scratched off immediately reforms.

In recent years there has been a commercial substitute for pure lead composed by adding antimony for the sake of greater hardness. While this increases the stiffness and decreases the necessary thickness for sheets of lead, it has not been exposed to all manner of weather conditions sufficiently long to determine whether the client's interests are absolutely safeguarded in employing it or not. Certain it is that pure lead used in the traditions of the past guarantees that the work will last a millenium. If the architect wishes to experiment so that future generations may profit by his experience, it is his privilege, of course. The discussion here will be confined to virgin lead.

A convenience in the designation of lead sheets is that the thickness expressed in 64ths of an inch equals the weight in pounds to the square foot, up to $\frac{1}{4}$ or $\frac{16}{64}$ inch, which is 16 pounds to the square foot. Thus $\frac{3}{64}$-inch-lead would weigh 3 pounds; $\frac{8}{64}$ or $\frac{1}{8}$ inch would be 8 pounds, etc.

A singular quality of solder, the alloy of tin and lead used generally for uniting parts of lead, is that it melts at a lower temperature than either metal singly. It has a brighter color than lead, causing a plaguey problem in lead cames (extruded sections for receiving leaded glass), since the soldered joints always obtrude because of their lighter tone.

ARCHITECTURAL DESIGN AND USAGE

ANY ONE observing the diversified historic employment of lead, and its adaptability for both casting and beating, might be inclined to assume that it could be substituted for almost any other material. But Viollet-le-Duc, not without good reason, maintains: " . . . that which gives to the lead work of the middle ages a particular charm, is that the means

employed and the forms adopted were exactly appropriate to the material. Like carpentry or cabinet work, 'plumbing' was an art apart which borrowed neither from stone nor wood in its design. Mediæval lead was wrought like colossal goldsmith's work." The designer should realize that just as he cannot hope to obtain the germane effect in using terra-cotta when executing a conception meant for stone, in the same manner is it disappointing to expect satisfaction from lead if the design be inappropriate.

There are not many restrictions in lead design placed upon the architect. If he will not require the detail to have the sharpness of a bronze casting (although it *can* be done), and if pierced designs have their most emaciated members at least ⅛ inch wide and ¾₆ inch thick, almost anything else his pencil desires can with propriety be executed. If there be undercuts these should be at a fair scale, like the parts of a statue or a capital, and not introduced in the intricacies of low-relief ornament. Perhaps the outstanding advantage of lead detail lies in the softness of the effects possible, and although it could be so wrought and cast as to have the undercutting and minute detail of bronze, it would mean sacrificing the natural virtues which it might better display. Old lead always has a genial, homely look, as though it relished being not too precise, and would rather romp with Tom Sawyer any day than play with little Lord Fauntleroy.

The methods by which lead was worked during the wrongly termed "Dark Ages" (and which still are continued in the best practice), involved first casting it in sheets on a rough bed of sand, and, on cooling, heating and bending it into a multitude of forms for leader heads, gutters, down-spouts, etc. Statues and vases were cast, sometimes in sand core moulds, or else by the *cire perdue* process more generally associated with bronze (pages 23–24). The French were prone to employ *repoussé* lead where the English might have used cast. These methods are similarly employed at present to secure moulded forms common in buildings, as cornices with or without ornament, running bands or panels with low or high relief, pierced insert designs (page 162), grotesques used as water spouts—in fact, all manner of architectural embellishments from spire to grade level. The few pages of illustrations which follow can give but a limited idea of the scope possible with the genial gray metal.

Aside from relief modeling, several means have been used to enrich lead ornamentation, or to employ it decoratively in combination with other materials. Gilding has such auspicious precedent as on the dome of St. Sophia and the ornamental lead work of St. Chapelle, while a painted and pierced ridge graces the Cathedral of Bourges. Sometimes certain parts are overlaid with tin, giving a brighter and

more silvery effect in contrast with the duller color of the lead; how this is done is explained in a later paragraph. Another alternative is to incise or cast the design in relief, preparatory to having the depressions filled with black mastic. Lead will allow itself to be nailed on without danger of breaking as a brittle metal might. In interiors it can be used with the complacency of pursuing the precedent set by one no less than Robert Adam himself in overmantel

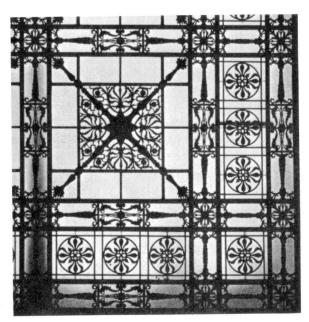

Fig. 202.—Portion of Leaded Skylight in Banking Room of the State Bank and Trust Company of Evanston, Ill.

Childs & Smith, Architects
The Linden Company, Craftsmen

adornment. In the Versailles treatment in bas-reliefs over doorways, clusters in high panels, and friezes or column capitals, lead was gilded in perfect imitation of the gilt bronze nearer the eye. Stone statues have sometimes had lead ornaments appended, stone slabs have been inlaid with lead to produce a grisaille effect (painting in gray monotone), and inscriptions in marble have been achieved with lead characters. Pierced ornamental plates have been used in combination with wood or iron. The surprising use of lead in early American wrought iron railings is dealt with in "Wrought Iron in Architecture: Its History and Craftsmanship," by the author.

The spire has always found artistic expression in lead, being used for that purpose before stone. The oldest existing lead survivor in England is at Long Sutton, where it was overlaid on rough boarding 1 inch thick; its height was 84½ feet. In Sir Lawrence Weaver's book "English Leadwork," he points out that, "since lead is the most efficient roofing material, in the leaded spire (which is the roof spiritualized) construction and symbolism have perfect meeting." Since lead expands it is advisable for the architect to be sure that all joints be rolled or locked, and because the problem is a highly specialized one, a lead roof should not be detailed without expert advice. Investigating similar workmanship and material which have withstood adverse conditions for several decades at least, is a precaution worth taking. The white and almost glistening patina of the lead is an æsthetic asset to any building, but of course cannot be expected to appear white where the air is not free from soot.

In order that the design not only look stable but actually be so, the lead must necessarily be sufficiently heavy so that it is creditably strong. Modern penny-wise, pound-foolish practice often tends to employ lead too thin. However, vases, small figures, etc., should be of moderately light metal so that they will not sag, droop or bend from their own weight, yet should be able to withstand the bumps of everyday life. Where supports are needed these should *not* be iron or steel, but brass or bronze because of chemical complications which are set up. Old work had the advantage of being used with water-seasoned timber, bereft of sap-acid which sometimes has a deleterious effect.

The architect should bear in mind when designing lead work how distant from the eye level it is to be placed on the building, so that ornament will be neither too small nor too delicate to be appreciated. Often cornice and gutter *motifs* are detailed as though they were to be of white wood work, but after being oxidized to a dark gray, they might almost be plain facias as viewed from the ground.

MODERN METHODS OF WORKING LEAD

ALTHOUGH different in many respects from bronze, lead has this similarity, that the best means of craftsmanship are no different now than in the period of its greatest accomplishments, minor details excepted. A recital of the methods at present employed varies but slightly from those of the mediæval artisan: whereas he used solder for uniting separate parts, the blow torch has now made possible the "burning" of joints, *i. e.* heating the lead at the juncture to the fusing point, and melting other lead into the crevice so that a unified mass results. The advantage of this lies in the uniform color imparted by the modern method, whereas formerly the addition of solder, containing tin, left a lighter color trace.

Compared to bronze or iron casting, that of lead is relatively simple. Assume that an architect desires a leader head similar to the ones on page 162, and has sent the full-size drawing and an approved plaster model for the ornament to the lead works. The craftsman would plan on first casting a sheet of lead the size of the four sides of the leader head when spread out flat. A bed of coarse sand would be prepared a bit larger than the required sheet of lead, and at sides and ends would be troughs to catch the surplus metal. The sand is specially prepared to be of certain moisture below, with new dry surfacing sand on top. The plaster model is then rammed into the sand at the proper place in relation to the location it is to have on the cast sheet. If there were any danger of the model's breaking, its counterpart might be made of metal, or, for a simple running ornament, the pattern units would probably be cast in some metal and nailed to a board to form the complete pattern which would be rammed into the sand. In the meantime the lead would be melted by a simple caldron affair, having sufficient capacity to hold the required supply of molten metal. Any supply of heat beneath the pot serves the purpose of melting the contents. At one end of the bed of prepared sand and extending its width, is a U-shaped reservoir which is filled with molten lead; when all is in readiness, it is dumped over on the sand bed which is slightly inclined. There is a deluge of running silver. The lead runs the length and breadth of the bed (about 9 by 3 feet, maximum), until its surplus overflows the sides, thus giving assurance that the sheet will be uniformly thick—in good practice at least ¼ inch.

It is fascinating to see the lead cool, with undulating waves of variegated color sweeping over its surface. Within a moment or two, when it is solid and cool enough to handle, the edges are cut down to the desired shape by a huge blade. The four sides are bent up to form an empty box, first scoring lines in the inside and then bending the sheet along them. Once the sides of the leader head are thus formed, the seam at one of the back corners is burned together; a bottom is added by similarly burning all around the lower edge of the four sides. The process of burning, as hitherto described, makes an absolutely homogeneous juncture.

FIG. 203.—CAST LEAD FIGURE OF PAN
(SIDE AND FRONT VIEWS)

Walter Gilbert and L. Weingartner, Sculptors
Cast by the Birmingham Guild, Ltd.

Not only the subject-matter is suitable to the genial material,
but the modeling as well, because of its simplicity and directness

The top of the down-spout is burned into the bottom of the leader head in the same manner. In burning lead a small blow torch is used, preferably fed by oxygen and hydrogen, because this combination is the "cleanest"; oxygen with coal gas is a possible substitute, or, still less desirable, acetylene. Incidentally, the torch can be used not only for joining parts, but for cutting fretted edges and profile designs. Down-spouts with or without ornament are cast in sheets, bent into shape, and the vertical seam at the back burned together; horizontal joints are also solidified by burning.

In lieu of ramming the model into the sand and casting the sheet with the ornament, the old French craftsmen's *repoussé* method may also be applied with good effect by expert artisans. The general form of the modeling is beaten out from the back of the sheet, which is then turned over and placed on a wood or pitch block to have the relief carefully modeled by beating it on the front face. If done by skilled craftsmen this method has all the virtues of incorporating intimate and personal feeling, while under the hammer of an inferior worker the result is not to be anticipated with pleasure.

Other than sheets, cast lead work does not vary from that of bronze as previously described (pages 21–27), in so far as preparation of the moulds is concerned. The distinction which the architect should bear in mind for lead work, however, is that his model should look as though it were designed in soft clay rather than carved out of brittle plaster of Paris, if the finished product is to appear genuinely characteristic for the material. The French sand used for bronze casting is purposely fine so that the metal will duplicate every minute detail of the modeling, while in lead it is an advantage if the sand, except for delicately ornamented parts or statues, be rather coarse so as to produce an uneven texture. The charm of old lead work is in good measure indebted to irregular surfacing, hence the advantage in casting it on a bed of coarse sand as set forth above.

Ornamentation of lead should be cast or beaten out from the sheet so as to be an integral part of it—never "sweated" on (applied by solder) if it is to be a first-class job. The craftsmanlike way of working lead would scorn any such temporary method as depending on the good grace of a little precarious solder to insure the ornament from falling off at some unexpected moment. The only place in which *applied* lead ornament plays a legitimate rôle is in the embellishment of some foreign material, as wood or stone, as mentioned under "Architectural Design and Usage" of this chapter (page 154).

Lead may be ornamented by applying tin to the surface of certain parts, since the latter always remains a brighter color. The initial step, where the lead is to be coated, is to scrape down the surface to a depth of about $\frac{1}{16}$ of an inch with a sharp tool in order to roughen it, and then dust rosin over the same area. A blow torch is applied to the end of a small wire of tin (held very near the lead) until the tin melts, and must be so manipulated that the melting metal runs only where wanted. The tendency is for the molten tin to run beyond the design limits, so that a steady and trained hand is required to restrain it. Tin is frequently used to embellish work with a monogram, date or simple design, but, when this is done, the distance from where it will be seen should be taken into consideration, as well as the inability of the artisan to work at too fine a scale.

A recent development to meet the demand for a less expensive product than bona fide lead, for such purposes as gutters and downspouts, has been to coat copper with lead. Methods have been evolved which simulate the cast lead surfacing to a surprising degree, and if a client has not the money to pay for genuine lead work but desires its color, it is worthy of the architect's investigation. The weight is greatly reduced as compared with that of pure lead; moreover, the stamping of ornament may be done. The oldest installation to date has an age of about ten years; in some cases it has been satisfactory, while in others the lead has scaled off. There are a number of products on the market, some infinitely better than others. In all copper work it must be remembered that under no condition should auxiliary steel or iron in any shape or form be used, but only brass or bronze. The entire work will have to be replaced within several years if iron supports, brackets, nails, etc., are utilized, because of the detrimental chemical effect.

The whitish patina acquired from atmospheric conditions will naturally vary with the modeling, exposure, etc., and is the most desirable color for lead. In the imitation of "antiques," the casting and century-old patina are simulated (?) within a single working day by heating the casting, washing it with hydrocholoric acid, and, while still hot, brushing with water and then drying it. The patina is uniform all over however, and apt to be easily rubbed off with one's finger. Another method of adding an antique complexion is to bury the lead in wet lime in order to eat away a part of the surface; on recovery it is washed with tea leaves or herbs to produce an aged brown effect. A third prescription involves painting the lead with thin oil colors and then applying what is variously known as ferrous sulphate, copperas, or green vitriol. The lead is then scorched, repainted, scraped and battered, which supposedly gives the effect of an antique which has at one time or another seen happier painted days. If the architect desires to turn lead a dark color without waiting for it to oxidize naturally, raw or boiled linseed oil will do the trick, while a deep, dark tone can be coaxed with an application of crude or machine oil.

Lead craftsmen are few and far between, and the architects who have used this hardy and artistic material are almost as rare. It seems unfortunate that a metal with the combined graces of all the others should have fallen into relative disuse since its great period of *Le Grand Monarch* in the festive days of French history. The present dearth of designers and artisans leads to the vicious circle of there not being extensive usage because there are but few capable workmen, and vice versa, there being such a limited employment for the metal that only a brave soul will risk his future in setting out to pursue its craft. The solution probably lies in the reawakening interest of the architectural profession and the public for the gray philosophic metal, willing to accommodate itself to pocketbook and design with equal grace, be it for high or humble state in portrait figure or down-spout.

FIG. 204.—LEAD TURRET WITH ORNAMENTATION, ST. THOMAS'S, FIFTH AVENUE, NEW YORK CITY

Cram, Goodhue & Ferguson, Architects
Henry Hope & Sons, Craftsmen

Fig. 205.—Lead Finial
FROM OLD ROUEN HOUSE

Photograph from Cliche L. P.

Fig. 206.—Vase of Lead-Bronze, Basin of Neptune, Versailles

Photograph from Cliche L. P.

Fig. 207.—Vase of Lead-Bronze, Basin of Neptune, Versailles

Fig. 208.—Lead Finial
FROM OLD ROUEN HOUSE

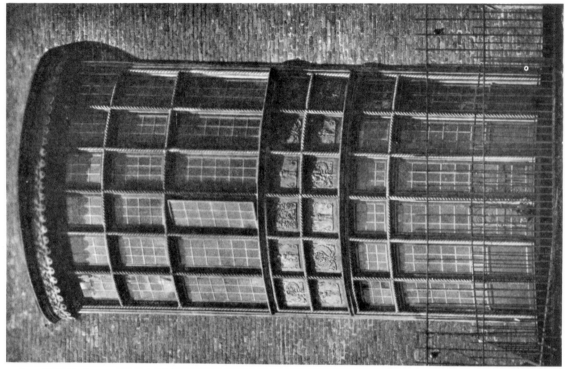

FIG. 210.—REPOUSSÉ LEAD BAY, RESIDENCE OF JACKSON
REYNOLDS, ESQ., NEW YORK CITY
H. T. Lindeberg, Architect   Klein & Kavanagh, Craftsmen

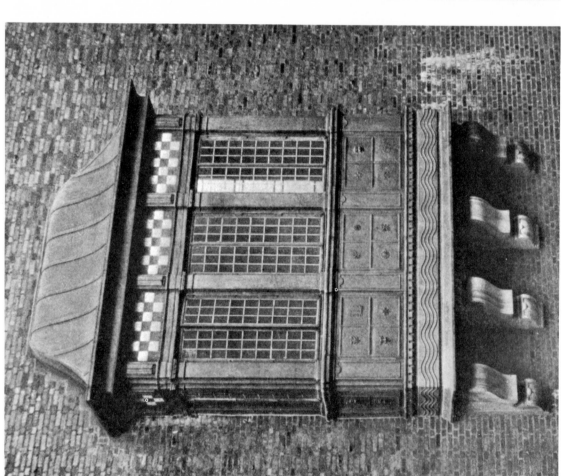

FIG. 209.—CAST LEAD BAY, DETROIT INSTITUTE OF ARTS, DETROIT
Paul Cret, and Zantzinger, Borie & Medary, Associated Architects
Henry Hope & Sons, Craftsmen

LEAD: ILLUSTRATIONS

FIG. 212.—LEADED ENTRANCE DOOR, NORTHERN STATES INSURANCE BUILDING, HAMMOND, IND.

Childs & Smith, Architects

G. Owen Bonawit, Craftsman

FIG. 211.—CAST LEAD FRONT (ABOVE GROUND FLOOR) AT DIGBE, ENGLAND

Buckland & Farmer, Architects

Henry Hope & Sons, Craftsmen

FIG. 213   FIG. 214   FIG. 215

FIG. 216 (TINNED IN PLACES)   FIG. 217   FIG. 218

FIG. 219   FIG. 220   FIG. 221

LEAD LEADER HEADS, SHOWING VARIOUS TYPES OF ORNAMENTATION
Figs. 213–218 inclusive, executed by Henry Hope & Sons, Ltd.; Fig. 219 by the Birmingham Guild, Ltd.; and Figs. 220 and 221 by
Klein & Kavanagh

FIG. 222.—PLAIN AND ORNAMENTED DOWN-SPOUTS IN CAST LEAD
Some of the characteristic rough surfacing can be faintly discerned on the second
from the left; those with ornamentation illustrate suitable enrichment for lead.
Executed by Henry Hope & Sons, Ltd.

FIG. 223.—ORNAMENTED GUTTERS IN CAST LEAD
The one in the lower right-hand corner is lighter in color where it has been tinned. All were executed by Henry Hope
& Sons, Ltd., with the exception of the one in the lower left-hand corner, which is by the Birmingham Guild, Ltd.

FIG. 224.—CAST LEAD CISTERN, NOW IN VICTORIA AND ALBERT MUSEUM. (ENGLISH, 1677)
Height, 2 feet 5 inches; width, 3 feet 11 inches; depth, 1 foot 9 inches

FIG. 225.—CAST LEAD CISTERN REMOVED FROM ROYAL AGRICULTURAL SOCIETY'S HOUSE,
12 HANOVER SQUARE, LONDON; NOW IN VICTORIA AND ALBERT MUSEUM
Height, 2 feet 6¾ inches; width, 3 feet 11 inches; depth, 1 foot 9 inches

ZINC

WHILE zinc has been used to some extent in roofing, ornamental cornices and the like, it has not found as great favor as copper, in spite of lesser cost for the raw material. Although it forms a thin basic carbonate, soft gray in color, which is somewhat of a protection from adverse atmospheric conditions, it should be kept painted on exteriors. In being stamped it cannot be annealed more than three times, and even before then sometimes cracks; copper can be annealed six or seven times. In America zinc found its greatest popularity several decades ago when the cost of material compared to that of the labor was considerable. Now that the proportionate cost of labor has increased to a point far in excess of raw materials, although copper is about three times as expensive as zinc, the greater ease with which the former is worked offsets the initial difference in price. Some of the best craftsmen prefer to supply copper even though zinc is specified, because of the more satisfactory manner in which deep and sharp stamping can be done and the greater longevity of the job when completed. Whereas the most ancient examples of copper are traceable for several thousand years, the oldest zinc products date back only about seventy-five years to the roofs of a number of Belgium and French buildings.

Zinc cannot boast of ancient usage in a pure state, as do other metals, although it has long been used as an alloy with copper. There is no trace of zinc in the bronze tools of Egypt or Greece, nor "in any appreciable quantity in European implements of the bronze period." * Possibly it may have been known indirectly to the Romans. "The bishops Ambrosius of Milan (374–397), Primasius of Adrumetum (sixth century), and Isidore of Seville (c. 570–636), refer in their writings to a substance, the addition of which to copper gave it a yellow color." * Church objects of Rhenish Byzantine style and later are of bronze with a yellow color, probably because of considerable zinc being present. The first English usage seems to have been at Champion, near Bristol, about 1760.

* "Bronzes," C. Drury E. Fortnum.

TIN

IN an unalloyed form tin has not been of great architectural importance except for lighting fixtures. It was known to the Greeks, judging from the use of an independent word designating it. To the Romans it was "white lead," and less useful than ordinary or "black" lead, as they termed it. Allied with copper it had found early usage in the formation of the common alloy, bronze, but employed by itself the earliest reference seems to be in the first century A. D.

At certain times during the mediæval period tin became the popular material for lanterns. Elaborate forms and details, pierced patterns and *repoussé* work, are readily made by virtue of its lightness and ease of working. At the close of the fourteenth century Dijon became noted as the centre of the lantern industry. The Spanish were not hesitant in recognizing the advantages of tin when making lamps in the shape of many-pointed stars. Andalusian tin lanterns were frequently gilded and painted, some having exquisite workmanship in calyx-like crowns, while others had colored panes of glass with painted armorial devices, suspended from long silken cords terminating in tassels.

American Colonial lamps, lanterns, sconces and candlesticks enjoyed popular favor over a relatively long period. The earliest were unpainted, but were ornamented by patterns composed of perforations; many were later elaborated by stencilling and painting. A favorite form included a conical top with a picturesque, diminutive dormer, surmounting a cylindrical shaft, and over-all such intricate perforations as to simulate filigree work. Reflectors were often set with pressed glass in geometric patterns and equipped with tin candle-holders, forming agreeable precedents for modern sconces.

The value of tin as an architectural metal is diminished because of the constant coat of paint it demands to withstand rust. Copper can perform the same tricks equally well if not better, and when unpainted acquires an enviable greenish patina instead of rust. The value of the designs executed in tin as lighting fixtures are none the less adaptable and valuable to other more permanent sheet metals, and offer apposite inspiration (page 178).

FIG. 226.—BYZANTINE HANGING CENTRE "LAMPADA," ST. MARK'S

The four double intersecting crosses not only compose one of the least exploited of forms, but offer a host of opportunities for small lights; in the present electrical era even the surmounting pierced sphere could throw out a soft diffused glow

LIGHTING FIXTURES

THE problem of designing lighting fixtures bobs up on the architect's horizon with the same infrequency as the proverbial blue-moon, and when it does, he is generally at a loss for documentary assistance. Although involving a new set of mental muscles, it can be converted into an engaging sport. The architect can, if he wills, accept the challenge of existing lighting fixtures by out-designing them at their own game. For who, on making a critical inspection tour of the products and by-products which comprise the architect's palette, has not felt the inadequacy of design in the illumination field, as compared with other forms of building accoutrements? Too often lighting fixtures fit neither the client's diminishing pocketbook nor the architect's increasing discrimination. It is not surprising that on occasion an enterprising designer-architect accomplishes his own luminous designs and seeks him out a metal craftsman who executes as he is bidden, with more economic and æsthetic result than if the architect had merely shrugged his shoulders and sighed that the stock in trade of lighting fixtures was so expensive and yet so unbeautiful. Perhaps there are numerous and excellent illumination products in existence which modestly hide from the architects' attention—yet we cannot help but hope, when in the near future no further progress be possible for those manipulators of clever brains who are now making radios and automobiles into *objets d' art*, that they will enjoy a happy and inviting future in the realm of lighting fixtures.

For the purpose of a sketch it not infrequently happens that it is necessary for the architect's organization to indicate something of a chandelier, bracket or lamp so that some competitive estimate of cost can be obtained. The illustrations which follow are therefore gleaned from a wide variety of sources, materials and purposes. Many of them will find no literal modern translation for want of parallel usage but are given for what suggestions they may offer. Others justify their presence by the beauty of execution, delicacy of ornament or lucid expression of the possibility in some particular material. The history of lighting fixtures is more specifically considered in conjunction with that of the various metals in successive periods when they were outstanding for one reason or another. The purpose here will therefore be not to collect in an orderly array the facts concerning the lineage, similarities or idiosyncrasies of illuminating forms, but to let representatives of all creeds and nationalities contribute what they may to germinate ideas for the design or embellishment of lighting fixtures.

Certain photographs will not fall into any accepted classes of illumination, but, as in the case of Empire brasses and bronzes, may offer pertinent suggestions as to *finesse* of ornament, subtlety of line or charm of silhouette. Reliquaries and incense-burners are obviously not lamps or chandeliers, yet there are so many hackneyed forms reused for lighting fixtures that certain illustrations which can readily be adapted by a facile pencil are included for mental refreshment. Instead of harking back to the accepted versions of trite forms for lighting fixtures, it might be provocative of invigorating design if the architect were to turn his attention to an entirely new set of forms. A case in point is the bronze "lampadario" (what could be a more expressive term?) of the Cathedral of Pisa (page 170) which was used by York & Sawyer as the inspiration for the chandelier of the universally admired Brooklyn Trust Company banking room. Exterior Florentine palace lamps, like those of the Strozzi and Guadagni, have so ingrained themselves in the public fancy that the national imagination seems almost stifled by them.

Although the architectural forms of the fabric of a building may have to be puritanically severe and there is but little elasticity in materials, or opportunity for the architect's imagination to take an exciting gallop, lighting possibilities offer this occasion. There is always the opportunity of employing chains for adding tremendously to scale, as in St. Sophia, Constantinople, which is perhaps the best example; or for chains to compose a fascinating design in silhouette (page 173), while in themselves there is a vast array of picturesque capabilities in detail (Figure 230). In short, if the designer will apply himself in creating lighting fixtures with the same assiduity as he busies himself varying the use of stone and brick, there can be produced a whole generation of inspired illumination prototypes which would take their place of honor with the heyday peers of the empires of Rome and Paris.

In the design of lighting fixtures one feature which should not be overlooked is the consideration whether or not the electric bulbs are to be frosted and exposed, or, on the other hand, enclosed within glass, mica, parchment, etc. A hanging lamp which may be perfectly in scale with a room, having its frosted bulbs exposed and arranged in tiers, will appear to be twice the size if glass or mica encloses them. A good example of such an improbable transition exists in an office building lobby in New York City by one of the best firms of architects. The fixture was studied with exposed frosted bulbs arranged in circular tiers, but the owner later had the sides of the lamp encased with translucent glass; whereas the fixture had formerly taken its scale from the numerous small sources of light and enjoyed the ornamental bronze details as a helpful supplement, after donning the glass envelope it looked like a suspended, illuminated ash-can with all scale annihilated.

Other considerations also should not be forgotten. One precaution is that bulbs be properly distributed within a glass enclosure (really a matter for consultation with a lighting expert) so as to determine whether or not there will be an equal diffusion of light and not a concentration at any one point from top to bottom, unless such an excess of light be an asset and not the usual detriment to the design of the fixture as a unit. Perhaps the most difficult phase of all for the architectural designer is the departure from the usual four-sided solid he is accustomed to visualize, into circular, octagonal and irregular shapes designed to be seen from below. Not only do numerous or curved sides complicate things, but the nature and suspended position offer vistas through the fixture, increase the importance of the decoration underneath, and, unless carefully considered, will exclude the top part from even

showing when viewed from below. Large fixtures in important rooms should always have a model put in place at the proper height before being executed, even when furnished by the best designers of the foremost fixture companies; in fact, the leading architectural offices make such trial models a part of the lighting contract.

In the composition of a building almost every known architectural form has been exploited, from the Babylonian set-back to the Colonial cupola, with such vigor that only an occasional new hocus-pocus of silhouette simulates a "new note." The opportunities for originality seem to narrow themselves to a more colorful employment of materials, a wider variety of massing, and a greater exploitation of lighting effects. Distinguished progress may be equally assertive in the single lamp, chandelier, or candlestick, as in the general illumination of a single room or the exterior of an entire building. Flood lighting is only in its infancy. Advertising managers agree that since the innovation of the moving (exterior) electric sign nothing new in this field has been invented, and that a fortune awaits him who can turn the trick. The effect of the color of lighting on the senses and emotions—producing a sense of warm welcome or chilly restraint—offers a maze for research only slightly explored. Yet it too is a challenge to the architect, for unstudied cold lighting may rob his architecture of all humanity and warmth, and leave it for the daws of unfair criticism to peck at.

The illustrations in this chapter do not pretend to foment any revolutionary or fortune-making ideas, but seek rather to take the architectural eye from the tomb rails and counter-screens below, to the instruments of light above. If none of them can be blue-printed and used without adaptation, all the better, for both they and the designer will profit by re-study. May they get along famously and be a stimulus to each other in producing results in character with this day and age!

FIG. 227.—TIN AND GLASS WALL SCONCES
(SEVENTEENTH-CENTURY AMERICAN)

FIG. 228.—HANGING LAMPS FROM POMPEII AND HERCULANEUM, NOW IN NATIONAL MUSEUM, NAPLES

Photographs of Figs. 229 and 230 by L. Ollivier

FIG. 229.—EMPIRE WALL BRACKET,
FONTAINEBLEAU

FIG. 230.—LOUIS XIII CHANDELIER,
FONTAINEBLEAU

Both of these lighting fixtures compose well, but the chains in Fig. 230 are particularly full of suggestion

FIG. 232.—THE SEVEN-BRANCH CANDELABRUM, MILAN CATHEDRAL
The six side branches date from 1562 when they were presented to the Cathedral, but the stem and base are probably of twelfth- or thirteenth-century origin. (14 feet wide)

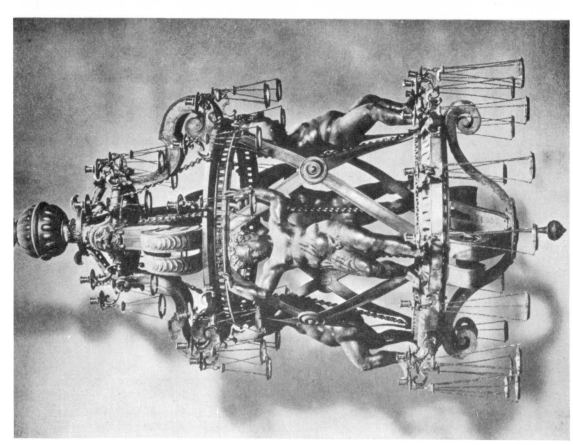

FIG. 231.—BRONZE LAMPADARIO, PISA CATHEDRAL. (V. POSSENTI)
This dexterous composition is called the "Lamp of Galileo," because (?) he evolved his laws of gravity from observing it as a pendulum. (Diameter of lower ring about 42 inches)

FIG. 235.—INCENSE-BURNER IN NATIONAL
MUSEUM, FLORENCE. (SIXTEENTH-
CENTURY ITALIAN)

As a hanging fixture this is complete, except
perhaps, for perforations in a modified bottom

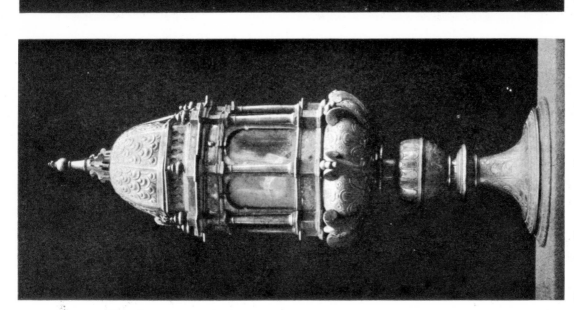

FIG. 234.—INCENSE-BURNER, MUSEO DELL' OPERA,
ORVIETO. (SEVENTEENTH CENTURY)

Add glass or mica on the inside of the perforated design, and the lighting fixture metamorphosis is completed

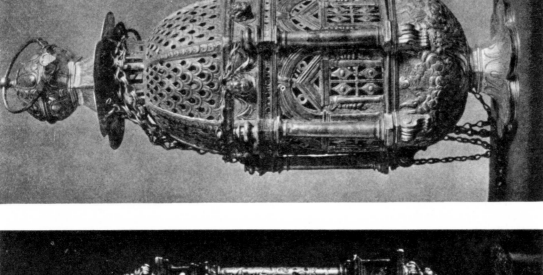

FIG. 233.—RELIQUARY, CHIESA DI OGNISSANTI,
FLORENCE. (SEVENTEENTH-CENTURY
FLORENTINE)

This presents a number of lighting fixture possibilities—
hanging or standing, with perhaps a transparent dome

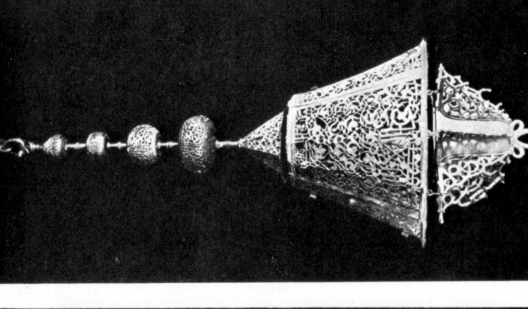

Fig. 236.—Silver Lamp, Chiesa della SS.
Annunziata, Florence. (Sixteenth century)

Fig. 237.—Moorish Lamp, Mosque of the
Alhambra, Granada

Fig. 238.—Gothic Censer, now in the
Victoria and Albert Museum

These three illustrations, taken from widely different origins, have one quality in common—that of being logically designed. There is a reasonable, evident scheme of composition underlying each of them, which many modern lamps totally lack

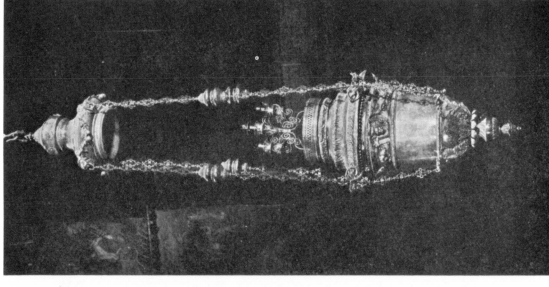

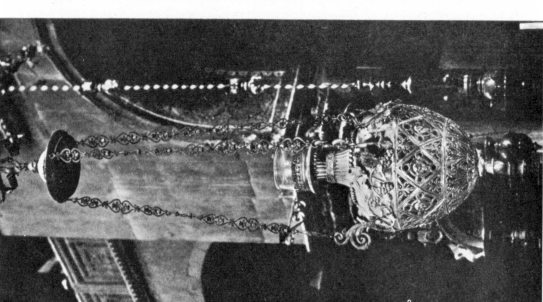

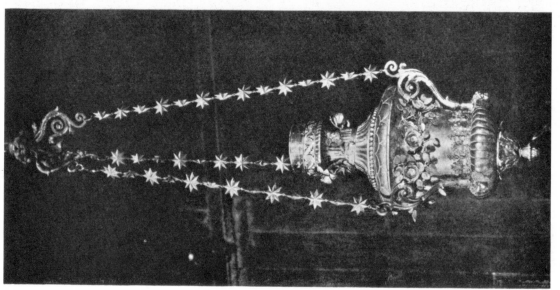

FIGS. 239, 240 AND 241.—THREE SILVER LAMPS FROM ST. MARK'S. (LEFT AND CENTRE ONES BY LO-
RENZO AND PIETRO FAURO, RIGHT ONE BY JACOPO VANZEL; CENTRE ONE ABOUT 22 INCHES EXTREME WIDTH)

These hanging lamps are distinctive not only for their unusual profiles and fitness of ornament, but for the fascinating use of chains. Each link bears the stamp of careful study, and adds a definite contribution to the *ensemble*

FIG. 242.—GILDED AND ENGRAVED EIGHTEENTH-CENTURY ITALIAN LANTERNS, BOLOGNA.
(FROM THE MEDICINA, S. GREGORIO, AND S. BARTOLOMEO)

While exhibiting some of the unfortunate frothiness of the Baroque, happily enough these "lanterns" on standards are not confined within the limitations established by the Strozzi and Guadagni lamps

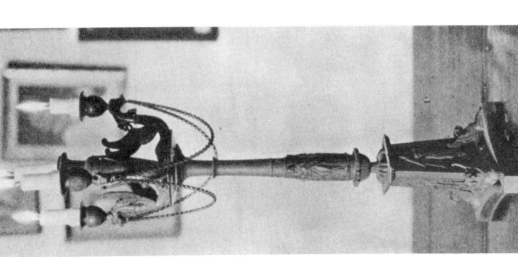

Fig. 243.—Empire Candelabrum by Jean Thomire (1750–1842)

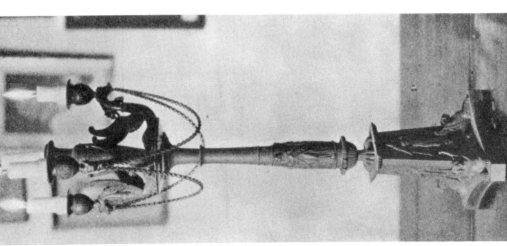

Fig. 244.—Bronze Empire Candlestick, one of a pair, once belonging to Joseph Bonaparte

Fig. 245.—Bronze Empire Candelabrum by Percier, now in the Louvre

French artistry and proficiency in bronze showed itself to no greater advantage than in the realm of lighting fixtures; even when usual forms were employed, it was with new and distinguished interpretation

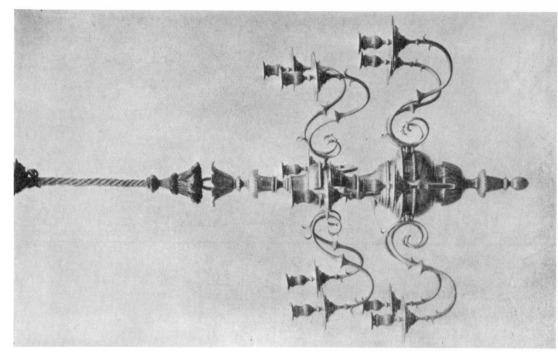

Courtesy of Metropolitan Museum of Art

FIG. 248.—BRASS CHANDELIER ATTRIBUTED TO
THE ADAM BROTHERS. (1750–75).

Courtesy of Victoria and Albert Museum

FIG. 247.—FRENCH ORMOLU WALL BRACKET.
(1750–60)

Executed by Jno. Williams, Inc.

FIG. 246.—BRONZE CHANDELIER WITH
NOTEWORTHY CHAINS

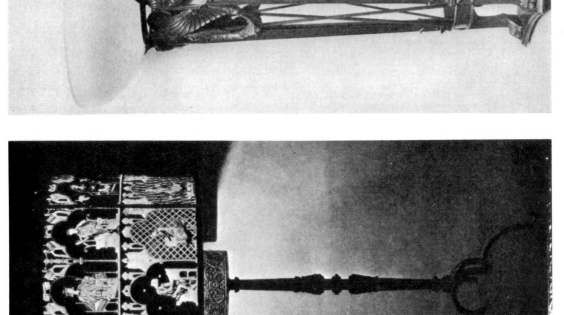

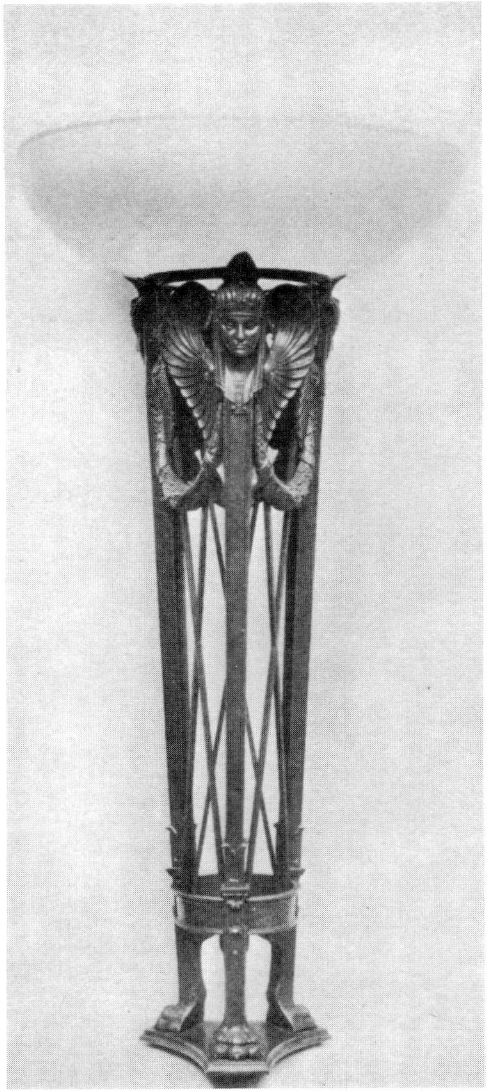

FIG. 251.—BRONZE LAMP STANDARD,
UNION BANK OF SCOTLAND, GLASGOW

James Miller, Architect
H. H. Martyn & Co., Ltd., Craftsmen

FIG. 250.—LAMP BY WARREN E. COX, WITH
MODERN SHADE AND OLD SPANISH GOTHIC
SPINDLE FOR STEM

The shade is a free interpretation of the Blanche of Cas-
tile Illumination, done as an etching on genuine vellum

FIG. 249.—EXTERIOR BRONZE LAMPS, FIRST
NATIONAL BANK OF BOSTON, BOSTON

York & Sawyer, Architects
Gorham Company, Craftsmen

FIG. 252
From the Frederick Richardson Collection

FIG. 253
From Boston, hung on Liberty Tree

FIG. 254
From Nash House, Hurley, N. Y.; no glass.

FIG. 255

FIG. 256

FIG. 257

From the Collection of the late Frederick Richardson, Salem, Massachusetts

AMERICAN COLONIAL LAMPS OF PERFORATED TIN AND GLASS

CURRENT DEVELOPMENTS

What is new now may be antedated to-morrow, yet within a few years it will be interesting to recall what in Anno Domini 1928 were considered new adjuncts to architectural expression.

ENAMELLING

BRIEFLY described, the craft of enamelling* consists in fusing special, ground, colored glasses on to metal. This is accomplished by adding the "enamel" to the surface of the metal in powdered form, either as a fusible silicate or colorless glass mixed with metallic oxides, and firing and re-firing with additional powder until the desired thickness has been reached, *i. e.*, when it is level or a little higher than the partitions between the metal cells. The entire surface is then polished down until it is an even smoothness. It is a curious fact that unless the metal and powdered glass are absolutely free from any physical impurities, such as dust, the firing will cause the enamel to bubble and blow up. Almost any color and any shade can be obtained; the most difficult to produce is red. Each color has a different fusing point, which means that if a plate has six colors it may have to be fired fifteen times. Naturally it is an expensive and difficult process because of the successive firings, and because on the last fusing the right temperature may not be obtained and the entire process may have to be done over again. On completion the colors are absolutely permanent.

The art is an ancient one, extending as far back as early Chinese civilization, and producing outstanding examples in the Ming period (1368 to 1643). At various periods particularly splendid enamelling has been produced, as by the Egyptians, by the French (particularly at Limoges), and by the Italians during both mediæval and Renaissance periods, and later with less artistic results continuing into the nineteenth century. The reason that enamelling is classed in this chapter is that until recently its usage has been more or less confined to jewelry, medals, vases, plaques, altar crosses, triptychs, and the like, but it has now begun to embellish twentieth-century architecture.

Modern commercial advertising, in its constant search for attractive displays with but little cost in upkeep, is expanding its usage of

* This does not refer to any liquid application.

champlevé enamelling (covering the surface between little metal partitions with opaque color) in combination with iron, bronze, brass or steel backgrounds. The results are the designer's delight, in that whatever can be represented on paper by the thickness of a line can be translated into enamel work. The best craftsmen have succeeded in producing name plates, signs, fascia lettering, memorial tablets and the like, which are a pleasure to remember because of the wide range of color and design possibilities, combined with jewelry-like execution. The added attraction of combining any of the metals with lettering, silhouettes or ornament in color, cannot be other than a business asset for the client and a colorful opportunity for the architect (page 180). For the hanging sign the least expensive means seems to be a combination of vitreous enamel with iron.

The designer has some few limitations in working with enamel which he should observe, yet there is so much elasticity and scope, that he who will not delight in this medium must indeed be a prosaic sort. The metal cell partitions can be reduced to the thickness of light cardboard and the inlay colors made to match almost any sketch submitted. The usual difficulty in other mediums in obtaining exact reproduction of the refinements which are the basis of fine lettering, is obviated in the enamelling process because of the minute scale it can reproduce. Any color scheme which the architect may desire can be secured, providing each unbroken color area does not exceed 6 square inches, and the largest single panels be no greater than 2 by 3 feet, or 6 square feet. Beyond that size it is difficult for the metal surface to be uniformly heated so that the enamel may "fire" evenly. Reference to Fig. 267 will illustrate the manner in which the design must be broken up by the metal partitions.

As contended under the chapter on "Lighting Fixtures," one of the most fertile fields for architectural achievement and development in the future lies in the introduction of color. Exterior exposure with attendant moisture, gases, and dirt, has until recently defied the success of a permanently colored building material to be used on a small scale. Until the introduction of enamelling no entirely successful material had been found. Happily enough this product is resistant to acid and all atmospheric conditions, and, because of its absolute smoothness, offers no inducement for soot and dust to

when the expense of their execution was not as prohibitive as now, yet a charm equal if not superior can be secured by the use of colored enamel. The full depth of possibilities of enamel has not been plumbed as yet. Opportunities are offered for: dropping hackneyed mouldings and replacing them by coruscating lines of color; substituting color inlay for carved ornamentation; introducing decorative lettering and signs as embellishment in color (as on

FIG. 258.—REPRODUCTION IN COLOR OF ENAMEL URN OVER ENTRANCE OF NATIONAL PROVINCIAL BANK, LEWISHAM, ENGLAND

See page opposite for view of entire entrance

F. C. R. Palmer and W. F. C. Holden, Architects
The Birmingham Guild, Ltd., Craftsmen

cling; in the event that dirt collects, ordinary window cleaning is more than sufficient for restoration needs. Another advantage in enamelling is that it offers a means of employing color on a small scale at entrances and points of particular interest where it will attract the eye. It gives the designer an entirely new medium and a rejuvenated palette with which to detail distinctive architecture for a discriminating client who will enjoy departing from the humdrum gray-black-and-white code of the preceding century. Glass and marble mosaics, such as enhance Romanesque cathedrals of southern Italy, are emblems of an age

mediæval German houses); picking out in color the arabesques on door pilasters, caps and bases of windows, doors and counter-screen grilles; and so on and on to the designer's endless gratification.

The first building to use enamelling extensively on the exterior will be the new National Radiator Company Building, London, by Raymond M. Hood, designer; Gordon Jeeves, resident architect. Black granite is used between window openings, but the cornice friezes, the lighting devices and the ground floor doorways are done in enamel of varying shades of green, yellow, lemon, red, and gold (page 182).

FIG. 259.—CHAMPLEVÉ ENAMEL AND BRONZE ENRICHMENTS, WROUGHT IRON ENTRANCE,
NATIONAL PROVINCIAL BANK, LEWISHAM, ENGLAND
F. C. R. Palmer and W. F. C. Holden, Architects   (See page opposite for detail in color)   The Birmingham Guild, Ltd., Craftsmen

FIG. 260.—DETAIL OF ENTRANCE DOORWAY IN COLOR

FIG. 261.—DETAIL OF SHOW-WINDOW IN COLOR

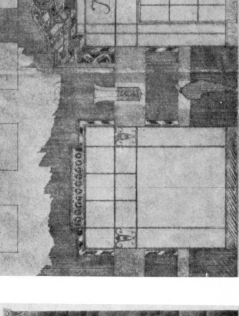

FIG. 263. — ELEVATION OF ENTRANCE AND ONE OF FLANKING SHOW-WINDOWS

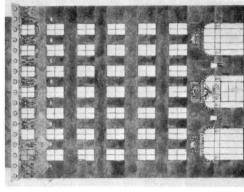

FIG. 262.—ELEVATION, CORRECT FOR GENERAL PARTI BUT SUPERSEDED IN SOME DETAILS

FAÇADE OF NATIONAL RADIATOR BUILDING, LONDON, OF BLACK MARBLE ORNAMENTED BY CHAMPLEVÉ ENAMEL IN GREEN, YELLOW, LEMON, RED AND GOLD
Raymond M. Hood, Designer; Gordon Jeeves, Resident Architect
The Birmingham Guild, Ltd., Craftsmen

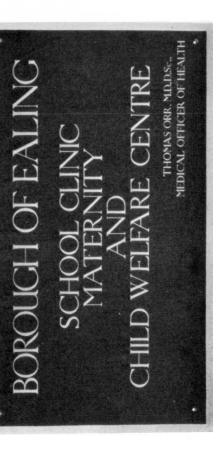

FIG. 267

FIG. 266

FIG. 265

FIG. 264

BOROUGH OF EALING

SCHOOL CLINIC
MATERNITY
AND
CHILD WELFARE CENTRE

THOMAS ORR, M.D.,D.Sc.
MEDICAL OFFICER OF HEALTH

FIG. 269

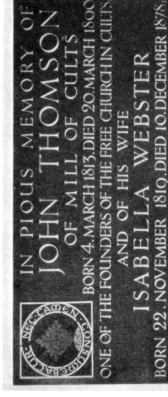

FIG. 268

Figs. 264, 268, and 269, bronze tablets with incised colored enamel; Figs. 265 and 266, bronze tablets silver-plated with incised V-section letters; Fig. 267, bronze with colored enamel, 6 feet high in six sections. (Executed by the Birmingham Guild, Ltd.) The lettering is particularly commendable.

FIG. 272.—WROUGHT MONEL METAL GATES AND
LUNETTE, WEST PALM BEACH, FLORIDA
Palm Beach Forge, Craftsmen

FIG. 271.—
CAST MONEL
PILASTER
Gorham Com-
pany, Craftsmen

FIG. 270.—WROUGHT MONEL METAL GRILLE,
WEST PALM BEACH, FLORIDA
Palm Beach Forge, Craftsmen

MONEL METAL

"Monel Metal" is a registered trade-mark name representing a "technically controlled nickel-copper alloy," which has been on the market since 1905. In general it may be said to consist of 68 per cent nickel, 27 copper, and the remaining five parts of iron, manganese, silicon and carbon. It has found extensive and dependable usage in a number of industrial fields, and recently has been artistically used for ornamental metal work. It is unique among the architectural decorative metals in that it combines the possibilities of casting and forging the same material. Where the architect has an appropriation sufficient to buy bronze, but wishes to embody the sympathetic hammered qualities of wrought iron, yet dislikes painting the latter or depending upon the janitor's oiling it properly, monel metal agreeably offers its services. In appearance it is very similar to nickel, or any of the so-called "white metals." It will take a high polish and appear like polished nickel, while other parts may be left dull—obviously a color asset in design where contrasting panels or surfaces are desirable. When exposed to the weather it does not rust but assumes a silver-gray patina which halts further corrosion, in fact, the metal is resistant to far more violent enemies than atmosphere, and withstands everything except a few acids, alkalies, and salts, as well as oxidation at high temperatures. In its repertoire are forging, casting, welding, annealing, soldering or brazing, spinning and drawing.

In being forged (like wrought iron) monel metal is harder to work than iron and is more akin to the nickel steels. While the labor and material are more expensive than for wrought iron, there is no upkeep necessary for the finished product and almost the same effects can be obtained. As far as the craftsman* is concerned, the usual forge fire is not used with good effect because monel tends to assimilate sulphur at the forging heat. Low-sulphur oil and gas are both preferable to coke or coal. A muffle type of furnace, or a reverberatory heating furnace, are better suited to the purpose.

The practice of casting* monel metal is highly technical, by including some of the characteristics of those for both steel and bronze. As far as the architect is concerned, the important shop item is that shrinkage is ¼ inch to the foot, or double that of cast iron. In his design he can incorporate *motifs* which can be either cast or wrought, and can be assured that even though exposed to the weather, the metal will not suffer.

* Craftsmen interested in monel metal can obtain complete information from The International Nickel Company, 67 Wall Street, New York City; *Bulletin* 121—"Hints on Sand Casting Monel Metal," and *Bulletin* 108—"Forging."

FIG. 273.—MONEL METAL GRILLES, ELEVATOR HALL AT 527 FIFTH AVENUE, NEW YORK CITY
Designed by Raphael Studios   Executed by Handcraft Iron Corporation

DEPOSITING COPPER ON GLASS

Among the many interesting uses to which electrolitic action has been directed is that of depositing copper on glass. The advantage to the architect is apparent—in his need for illuminated signs he has for too long been compelled to accept clumsy glass letters which fitted into pierced metal sheets. He was unable to procure the delineation of his carefully studied details and often saw with dismay an exit doorway ruined by the frightful lettering above, or, what more frequently happened, after the completion of the building the owner added signs which the architect did not care to claim as his own. However, being able to design the lettering or any type of ornament, for lighting fixtures, signs, marquises, running bands of illuminated ornament in cornices and friezes, etc., opens up a pleasurable field for the designer which hitherto was unpleasant even to contemplate.

The shop process consists in cutting out a stencil, which minutely follows the architect's full-size detail (a knife can of course be as accurate as a pencil line), after which the stencil material is glued to the glass selected (translucent or semiopaque), and retaining the part to be illuminated as the solid portion of the stencil. The areas to be covered by a copper deposit thus exposed are then sand-blasted to a certain depth and a conducting coat applied. The glass thus prepared (with the stencil covering the portions to be illuminated and the remaining portions sand-blasted and coated with a conducting agent) is put into a tank where the electro-deposition of copper takes place. After the product is removed, the copper is an integral part of the whole and cannot chip or scale off.

The use of this commendable medium is still but in its infancy. Signs have been made but the field it opens to ornamentation for skylights, sidelights, lunettes, lighting fixtures, running bands of ornament in and around ventilating grilles (so as to remove the curse of eternally black voids in rooms otherwise carefully studied)—all these and many more should find ready adaptation of this process. For the first time it seems possible to utilize the necessity of illuminated signs for decorative and artistic betterment, so that what formerly was the despair of the architect can now become an opportunity for additional color and sparkle in a harmonious manner. The minimum width of the deposit at any one point is a shade under $\frac{1}{16}$ inch; the smallest possible opening is a square a little under $\frac{1}{16}$ inch on a side.

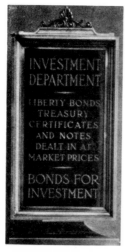

FIG. 274.—BANKING ROOM SIGN

FIG. 275.—DECORATIVE GLASS PLAQUE

FIG. 276.—CORNER OF CEILING-LIGHT DIFFUSER, SEDGEFIELD CONTINENTAL HOTEL, GREENSBORO, NORTH CAROLINA
Nathan Harris, Architect

These three illustrations (executed by the Frink Company) indicate some of the many possibilities in depositing copper on glass

STEEL

Chemically, steel is much the same as wrought iron and consequently is often employed in the same way. Not infrequently when the latter is specified, the former is used with no one being the wiser—for a while. It is not as ductile and tough as Norway or Swedish iron and will rust the easier. There is a difference in color but this can be so cleverly camouflaged that it is next to impossible for the non-specialist to differentiate.

A new and valuable innovation has been perfected in England whereby chromium is fused with steel (not merely plated) to produce a "stainless" quality. It is used on the undersea parts of ships and even there retains its finish, be it polished, bright or dull. The only cleaning agent needed is soap and water. Unfortunately it is about three times as expensive as bronze, but that is offset by the valuable introduction of silver in the color palette for shop-front, elevator cab, counter-screen, etc. It is best used in flat surfaces since it does not cast into moulded forms readily. Particularly advantageous use has been made of it in combination with enamelling. As modern upkeep costs in labor continue to soar it may be that chromium-steel will become economically inexpensive for surfaces requiring constant attention to eliminate finger marks, as on elevator cabs, counter-screens and shop-fronts.

FIG. 277.—PIERCED AND REPOUSSÉ PANEL OF FIRTH'S STAYBRITE STEEL
Birmingham Guild, Ltd., Craftsmen

ELECTROPLATING

Employing electrolysis in metal work has begun to work its wonders, not only in substituting for laborious damascening, but in coating one metal with another for protection or better appearance. At the present writing there are a number of experiments under way which sooner or later should prove practical and improve metal products. Our knowledge concerning the permanency of many of them is unfortunately curtailed because of the short time certain practices have been employed, so that it is yet too soon safely to make predictions or recommendations.

Electrical means have successfully been employed in imitating damascene work, but of course the result is more mechanical-looking than the bona fide mediæval prototypes. For certain usages where the work does not serve as jewelry it can be quite as serviceable and is, of course, infinitely cheaper. The background metal is coated with wax, as copper is when its surface is prepared for etching; the design is scratched on, exposing the metal where it is to be "inlaid," and the metal thus prepared is then submerged in acid identical with the etching process, until sufficient metal has been bitten away for the purpose to be served. The parts to be "inlaid," which have just been eaten out by acid, are then treated with some conducting coat. This will assimilate a metallic deposit when the metal has been submerged in a tank with anodes and cathodes properly arranged for the deposit of a foreign metal in the bitten grooves or areas.

Bronze has been successfully silver-plated, as in the Harvard Memorial plaque (page 183).

Niello (any dark inlay in metal—often a metallic alloy of sulphur with silver, copper, lead, etc.) is a simple form of ornamentation for bronze work, particularly where the cost of raised ornament would exceed the client's allowance. It is simply a matter of etching out the desired pattern with acid as described above and applying whatever color alloy is selected (pages 34, 35, 77) on the basic metal when it is hot.

The ever baffling problem of preserving wrought iron without painting it and not losing all complexion of its forging, may perhaps be solved by placing the iron work in a bath and electrically depositing a thin film of cadmium. Chromium has also been tried, and if it can be perfected will probably be superior, but at the present writing it refuses to deposit in the nooks and crannies, confining itself to the broad open spaces. Cadmium behaves better by distributing itself all over without discrimination. How long it will serve as a rust protector on exterior work is still in question; three years is now hoped for, although it may last longer.

CHEMICAL SURFACE ACTION

A process used since 1915 for protection from atmospheric corrosion for iron, steel, and other ferrous alloys, consists in converting the surface into insoluble phosphates by means of chemical action, so that it becomes insoluble in water and permanent in the air. If necessary to remove grease this is accomplished by cleaning through sand-rolling or blasting, if not chemically. The material to be treated is then submerged in a heated bath, or solution, of patented chemical composition, of complex metallic salts, composed largely of iron and manganese phosphates. In the bath the evolution of hydrogen energetically takes place for about fifteen minutes, but gradually abates and finally ceases after a treatment of an hour to an hour and a half. This action dissolves minute particles of iron from the surface and immediately replaces them by phosphates contained in the solution; this new surfacing becomes a part of the material which therefore cannot chip or peel off. One of the advantages of the process is that the surface remains prac-

tically the same as previously, being increased only by the negligible thickness of from 5 to 7 millimeters (⅒ of an inch), instead of being increased all over by a skin coating as in electroplating, galvanizing, etc. It would be a useful application in the case of cast iron, which generally receives a final coat of black paint; the phosphate surfacing is a uniform matte black, but at the same time provides an excellent base for painting or enamelling. The only installation necessary is a few tanks large enough to receive grilles in whole or in part, or whatever the craftsman will be apt to execute. Its advantage over painting is that it requires no additional attention, and none of the sharpness of the ornament is lost. Its usage abroad and in this country is acclaimed by those employing it. Such prominent manufacturers as the Western Electric Company and the Packard Motor Car Company utilize it. The outside of the motor of Lindbergh's famous "Spirit of St. Louis" was protected by this processing of the surface.

SPECIFICATIONS

HE architectural specification writer usually finds himself in the same predicament with each succeeding job—that of starting on it when it was supposedly complete a month previous. Constant inquiries as to when the document will be ready drives the harried writer to making the best he can of a tardy situation by resorting to ambiguous phrases instead of enumerating definite conditions, and to substituting, "etc.," where there should be detailed lists of required items.

The effect on the estimators of hastily written specifications is to make them dubious as what actually to figure on. To take all the phrases seriously which the specifications include as "protective measures" for the architect, would mean certain loss of the contract because of the estimate submitted; on the other hand, to disregard them entirely would cause certain loss if the work were awarded and enforced as described. The bid must lie somewhere between what the architect actually specified and what is covered by ambiguous clauses and a wholesale sprinkling of the too familiar "etc."

The net result of ambiguous specifications on the client is that he pays for what contractors have come to assume as so much "overhead." What is lost on one job because of indefinite wording must be made up on another. Occasionally a client may be fortunate in getting more than he has paid for, but not if the contractor can help it. Indefinite specifications cost the client more money, as a rule, than all the items of decoration which he considers "unnecessary trimmings." When there is to be a "cut" on a building operation after the estimates have been too high, unfortunately for the metal craftsmen it is their work which can be dispensed with most readily (according to the client), and the ambiguous specifications which have caused excessively high bids in all lines reduce the amount of their work.

The problem of writing an accurate statement of requirements for a building operation, to supplement the plans, is one which has always been a thorn in the flesh of metal craftsmen. Among other organizations the Allied Building Metal Industries of New York City has long been waging a campaign for definite specifica-

tions; we are indebted to them for a number of suggestions, and duplicates of pamphlets and letters which they have sent out from time to time toward the attainment of that goal. It is a problem of the vicious circle: the client unreasonably demanding completed plans and specifications; the architect attempting to meet these demands by rushing the specifications at the expense of their accuracy; the estimator being at a loss to give an accurate bid and consequently adding a certain percentage to protect himself against the *implied* wishes of the architect; the client having to pay "extras" and higher prices compared with a definitely specified job. If the architect could impress upon the client the necessity of adequate time allowance for the proper preparation of his plans and definite specifications, it would seem that the problem would be largely solved, for no architect purposely makes conditions more difficult for the contractors. But a client is not readily impressed by the fact that a certain length of time is necessary for preparing efficient specifications and that he will eventually profit by being patient; too often the land rental or a completion date for the building seems too grotesquely important to allow the architect adequate time for the execution of proper specifications. Sometimes, however, these are indefinite and riddled with ambiguous terms solely because the architect has not previously informed himself of general conditions, the scope of work, the manner of working the metals, or the desirable qualities of craftsmanship.

In the ideal specification the contractor will not have to search through all the plans, examining each square inch minutely, in order to determine what he is expected to furnish. Blueprints are variable vehicles at best. What may have been distinct pencil lettering on an original drawing when it was first made, may have blue-printed indistinctly; after the blue-print has been used by several estimators and been exposed to the sun, it is not to be wondered at if important items may be skipped in the unsatisfactory and unfair hide-and-seek system of estimating. The architect prefers not to list the work which is required for fear of omitting something, yet assuredly that should be no one's responsibility but his own. Moreover, it is not unfair to either client or craftsman if an item be omitted in the specification list, for the client is not paying for anything which he will not receive. Absence of a definite list often results in the most careless estimator being the successful bidder, for by counting short the items to be furnished he naturally lowers the amount of his bid. When shop-drawings, or lack of them, bring attention to the items not figured, it becomes the contractor's problem of so skimping on materials and workmanship that it will not mean a loss for him. The client is by no means then getting more than he paid for, and both the architect's reputation and the building suffer.

A not infrequent clause in specifications is that "the contractor shall do his work in accordance with the plans and full-size details which will be issued *later*." It is needless to repeat, in addition to what has preceded under "Estimate Drawings" for the various metals, that such a clause is in order only if the estimate drawings include details at no less than ¾-inch scale to the foot, but that if they are less than that in scale, estimating becomes a competition of relative mental guesses between the estimators as to what the architect may eventually demand.

Excerpts compiled by the Allied Building Metal Industries, typifying the ambiguous character of many specifications, may be illustrated by the following:

The work under this heading includes generally the furnishing of . . . (brief list of items) etc., and other miscellaneous iron work as shown on drawings or herein specified.

All miscellaneous iron work hereinafter specified or required by the drawings shall be furnished and erected as per plans and details, except such portions as are definitely specified to be furnished by the steel contractor and set by others.

The work under this heading includes generally . . . (brief list followed by "etc.").

The contractor shall furnish all labor, materials, tools, apparatus, equipment, etc., as required to fully complete this branch of work, as indicated on the drawings, herein specified and in general including the work and materials under the following headings . . . (list of headings in which "etc." is frequently used); also, all other necessary and incidental work in connection with the above and all such as is required by actual conditions at the premises.

This contractor shall furnish all the materials and perform all the work that may be required to fabricate and erect all the ornamental and miscellaneous iron of any description throughout the entire building and such other work as may be specified herein.

Sometimes specification writers fall into the habit of employing certain terms which are not quite sufficiently obsolete to be taken as a ritual of trumpeting which may be disregarded, and yet are so indefinite as to make for guesswork estimating. Among them are such phrases as: in general; as required, or, as may be required; as indicated; necessary and incidental; in connection with; required by actual conditions; includes generally; other miscellaneous items; hereinafter specified or required; as specified or indicated; "etc." (at the end of all lists of items or conditions).

In compiling items to be covered in specifications, the architect often has some sort of list he skims over to remind him of possible omissions. Any such method is of material help. For ornamental metal work specifications one of the most useful lists of the kind is one issued by the Allied Building Metal Industries, 18 West 34th Street, New York City, called, "Work of the Contractor for Ornamental and Miscellaneous Iron, Bronze and Wire Work."

In the methods of modern competition the honest craftsman often finds himself at a disadvantage because of the unfair, dishonest practice of certain competitors. It is becoming a regular trait, for which certain business men (not craftsmen) are known, to "go over the architect's head" and make business deals directly with the owner. This consists in convincing the client that the architect is incompetent to judge the merits of substitute materials, and that thousands of dollars can be saved by awarding the contract for workmanship and materials which are "just as good" as those specified. If such a contractor be sufficiently wily, he may even prove to the client's satisfaction that inferior materials and an uncertain quality of workmanship are superior to what the architect had specified. If such tactics are not resorted to before the work is estimated on, then they often follow the opening of bids if the unscrupulous business-getter has not been awarded the contract. Only recently the work for a large bank was won in fair competition by a reputable craftsman, and while the architect was drawing up his contract, one of the unfair competitors talked the owner into another contract without the architect's knowledge. There was nothing in the architect's agreement with the owner which permitted the former's interfering, even though the work as executed will be a blot on his reputation.

The remedy for this situation lies more in the architect's contract with his client than in the specifications. In the former it should be clearly understood, in case one bidder is successful by virtue of his estimate being lowest, that the client gives the architect full power to award a contract for such work and agrees to make none independently, and also, *in the event that it seems advisable to substitute cheaper materials, all estimators shall have the privilege of submitting new bids.* It takes no great intelligence to understand that if one contractor can save money by using less superior material, another bidder can do likewise, and that the client by awarding a contract on a new basis is doing so without the competition which would assure him of lowest prices. The architect who has not previously awarded contracts in metal work does well to investigate the reputations of all prospective bidders before allowing them to estimate, and if the ornamental metal contract be under a so-called "general contract," to name a list of craftsmen from whom general contractors may receive bids. This should always be insisted on if the architect wishes a creditable job, executed by honest bidders who will play fair with him and his client. He will find certain business enterprises in existence with whom he will never want to have any business dealings.

As new conditions arise in each building operation it would be advantageous if some index record were to be kept, so that when the same problem again presents itself it will not be necessary for the architect's organization to determine anew how it is best specified. For example, a subject as "Entrance Grille" could be placed at the top of a card (which in a card index would be listed under "Bronze"), and below it the names of the jobs specifying one, followed by the page number in the specification.

The best craftsmen are always willing to be of help to the architect, and in no way can they be of greater service than in the matter of specifications. In specifying his initial metal work, if the architect were to invite an expert craftsman to look over the plans—particularly the special conditions—he would invariably receive excellent suggestions which could advantageously be incorporated.

It is realized that it is impossible adequately to specify here each metal in skeleton form for all conditions, yet the material which follows should be helpful to the architect who has not previously used the decorative metals, or to

any one who has felt that his specification would bear improvement and comparison. Conditions are so variable for each building that when consulted many craftsmen frankly intimated that it was impossible to formulate an ideal specification which would assure the best of workmanship. However, it is better to begin with something than never to begin at all; as time goes by revisions and additions can be made by the architect in his practice, which will eventually result in a thoroughly useful and satisfactory form, as much so to him as to the craftsman.

Various craftsmen were requested to aid in the compilation of what would approach being a specification which would make it difficult, if not impossible, for the inferior workman or mere business-getter to compete with the conscientious craftsman who has the architect's and client's interests at heart. The general opinion was that it is impossible to specify the artistic standard which a product should attain, and that if the architect cannot limit his estimates to craftsmen whom he knows by reputation and workmanship, it is unlikely that a specification can exclude inferior products. However, the architect is often confronted with the problem of open competition, and must do the best he can with writing a stringent specification which will empower him to reject faulty work, and make it clear to all estimators at the outset that only the highest type of workmanship will be acceptable.

The following paragraphs are suggestions for "Notice to Bidders," "Workmanship," "Samples," and "Scope," which might be used in connection with all the various metals; specific conditions should be inserted where they are necessary.

Notice to Bidders.—It must be fully realized by all contractors before estimating on these specifications that the owner and architect are expecting and will pay for the artistic execution of the work, to be carried out according to the best traditions and methods of the craft. The interest of the metal craftsman in the execution of this work must be that of an artist taking personal pride in his craft, and not merely a commercial undertaking to reap as profitable harvest as possible. The architect will rigidly enforce both the word and spirit of these specifications, so that if the contractor is not artistically capable of executing the highest quality of metal work, it will only result in a financial loss to him to undertake this contract, because *any and all work which does not come up to the artistic standard set by the architect will be rejected and will under no circumstances be paid for.*

Quality of Workmanship.—It is the intent of these specifications to make it clearly understood that none but the highest type of craftsmanship will be accepted by the architect, who will be the sole judge as to the artistic merits and execution of the work. Bids will be accepted only on condition that the contractors submitting them acknowledge that the architect has the right to reject any and all work which does not come up to the quality of the craftsmanship of . . . (designate a sample submitted, a sample on view at the architect's office, or an executed piece of work in a certain building). The architect will accept no excuses whatsoever for the faulty or inferior execution of any of the work.

Samples.—The estimate for this work shall be accompanied by a sample of an executed piece of work done by the contractor submitting the estimate (or information concerning where his work may be examined, not too far distant), which will indicate clearly the capabilities of the contractor in the execution of this type of craftsmanship. If it does not measure up to the artistic standard established by the architect, who alone shall be the judge, the estimate will not be considered. When the contractor is awarded the contract for this work, all items not of equal or superior quality compared with the sample submitted (or like that of a designated building), shall be rejected and immediately replaced by the contractor at his own expense. If however he cannot execute the work satisfactorily, it will be awarded to another contractor. Such work which in the architect's opinion must be replaced in this way, will not be paid for. In submitting an estimate the contractor automatically acknowledges that he clearly understands *he will be paid only for such work as is accepted by the architect, who shall be the final judge in all matters of this nature.*

Scope of Work.—The work included in this section comprises the following items: (definite list follows, accompanied by reference to sheet numbers of plans and details, with no use of "etc.").

BRONZE

(Refer to page 28, chapter on Bronze, relative to "Some Practical Aspects.")

It is sometimes the practice of an architect to call for a sample of the actual work, accompanied by the craftsmen's bids. While this may be quite all right where a large contract of special character is involved, for the average job the craftsman has a perfect right to object to executing a sample at considerable expense to himself. The architect may take this measure in order to assure himself of the calibre of workmanship he will obtain, yet it is more equitable if he follow one of two other courses. He may require that with the filing of estimates a sample of similar workmanship shall be submitted, which will be typical of that which is to be executed, and which the architect shall retain for comparison with erected work, and with the authority to reject all craftsmanship which is inferior; or, he may have on view at his office a sample of the kind of craftsmanship which is required, and reserve the right to reject the work of the successful bidder unless it conforms in all respects to the sample figured on. Some procedure of this latter sort should be resorted to in the case of bronze work which is specified to be "hand chased," which may in the architect's mind mean merely removing "fins," or, at the other extreme, creating jewelry. From the usual specification expression, "hand-chased and carefully tooled," the estimators will have no conception of what is actually required, but with an actual sample on view, which will later be used as a gauge for the acceptance or rejection of work, there is a reduced possibility that poor bronze may be erected because the estimator successfully maintains not to have understood that such "hypercritical" inspection by the architect was to be expected. Furthermore, it prevents in good measure a poor foundry's receiving a contract on a low bid made possible because the foundryman believed he could bulldoze the architect into believing a non-chased or pseudo-chased job had been carefully tooled by hand. What is true for bronze is similarly true for cast iron (except for chasing, which is not possible in the latter).

To assure himself that there will be time to have new work made to replace what may be unacceptable, the architect should set a date a month ahead of the time when cast work is to be erected so that he can inspect it at the foundry; then if it is not up to the set standard he can order additional chasing or new castings to be made. In the event of an architect's organization having no samples which can be placed on view for the estimators to examine, he can refer to an existing building, definitely naming the part or portion which is to be considered par for his work.

Almost more important than the specifications in high-class bronze work, is the list of bidders. There are only a limited number of foundries capable of craftsmanlike artistry, yet for public work the architect cannot usually designate who shall and who shall not be permitted to estimate. His only recourse then is to make conditions so definite as regards quality of workmanship, that even the contractor who is endeavoring to palm off discreditable products is rigidly held to execute the work as specified, and is compelled to complete it sufficiently far in advance so that if rejected either he or another contractor has time to execute acceptable work without delaying the final completion of the building.

Several bronze foundries have suggested that in the specification a description of the operation and type of locks should be included, particularly as concerns any special hardware and any master-key instructions. The paragraphs on "Models" and "Delays" in the cast iron specification (pages 195–196) could appropriately be included in many cases, and (pages 191–192) for "Notice to Bidders," "Workmanship," "Samples," and "Scope."

In our efforts to obtain the best representative form of specifications for first-class bronze work, we requested all well-known foundries in and around New York City to send what they considered the ideal skeleton specification. While we are indebted to all of them for suggestions, the following is the most complete which was procured (from Jno. Williams, Inc., New York City), and should be suitable to serve as a guide for the architect who has not previously specified bronze:

Scope of Work.—The work under this section comprises the furnishing and setting of the counter-screen, partitions, check desks, stair, etc., balustrade and all the necessary hardware. Glass will be furnished under another contract.

Materials.—Drawn or rolled bronze shall consist of 90 per cent copper and 10 per cent zinc. In no instance shall the thickness be less than No. 12 B. & S.* gauge. Wherever tubing is used it shall be seamless. Cast bronze shall consist of 90 per cent copper, 7 per cent tin and 3 per cent zinc. In no instance shall it be less than 3/16 inch in thickness.

"Extruded bronze" shall be not less than No. 8 B. & S. gauge in thickness, and may be used for the hand rail of the stair, door frames, balustrade, etc.

Workmanship.—All bronze shall be straight, true, sharp, and free from sand holes, cold shuts, pits and any and all other imperfections. All work must be carefully jointed and fitted, metal to metal without filling, and no joints, rivets, screws or other fastenings shall be visible. Insofar as is possible, fastenings shall be made from the back or inside of the work.

* Brown & Sharpe.

All plain surfaces shall be filed smooth, fine emeried and brushed; the ornamental surfaces shall be chased and lightly brushed, and the whole left a natural color and given a thorough coating of wax. It is the intent of this specification to provide for work equal to the best product of the trade.

Cleaning.—After completion and just before the owner takes possession, the work shall be thoroughly cleaned; where the finish has been marred in the process of erection, it shall be restored so as to leave the work in perfect condition.

Sample.—Before the contract is signed, this contractor shall furnish to the architects, for approval, a sample showing the quality of the work to be performed on all bronze work under this contract. The workmanship of the sample must be satisfactory to the architects and all work performed under this contract shall be fully equal in every respect to that of the sample approved.

Models.—Full-size plaster models of all ornamental work shall be furnished by this contractor. These models shall be made by a competent modeler satisfactory to the architects, and they shall be executed in strict accordance with their details and instructions. The models shall be changed and altered at this contractor's expense until satisfactory to, and approved by, the architects.

In order to give some idea of how complete a bronze specification should be from the architect's standpoint, we are indebted to York & Sawyer, architects for the Royal Bank of Canada, Montreal, for the privilege of reprinting the specification of the bronze work for that building:

Models.—The owner will provide plaster models of all ornamental work. The models will be large enough to give the forms of all modeled work, but this contractor is to do any duplicating of them necessary to form his completed models for casting.

Setting.—The material shall be furnished and set in position in the building as may be required by the progress of the work. It shall be held in position with all the necessary anchors, expansion bolts, etc., secured to the masonry work, or by other approved means as may be required to secure it in place permanently.

Drilling and Cutting.—All drilling and cutting of masonry and other parts necessary for the installation of the work comprehended by this specification shall be done by this contractor.

Workmanship and Materials.—All work included in this contract shall be fabricated and erected in the best manner by skilled mechanics. Defective work of any kind, whether in materials or workmanship, will be rejected by the architects, and such material shall be removed from the premises and replaced with work satisfactory to the architects and without additional cost to the owner.

Unless otherwise noted all cast bronze shall be not less than 3/16 inch in thickness, extruded bronze not less than 1/8 inch in thickness, bronze plates not less than 12 gauge, drawn bronze tubing sections not less than 14 gauge; all gauges referred to herein being Brown & Sharpe.

All cast work must be clean, sharp and true; free from sand holes, rough spots or other imperfections; the metal to be chased and worked over until perfectly satisfactory to the architects. All castings shall be made from metal patterns, which are to be cut in every way to a duplicate of the approved models.

All the fine or ornamental castings of either bronze or iron are to be moulded in French sand, the moulds to be oven-dried in the most approved foundry practice.

The castings when made shall be a duplicate of the approved model or pattern; a clean, sharp, artistic product.

The castings must be of sufficient size and thickness of metal to insure perfect work; and the required thickness of metal to insure perfect work and the required strength for the purpose for which they are intended. Castings which are not rabbeted shall be cast with lugs, as may be required, for connection to adjacent sections and other work, and shall be fitted together with shoulders and brackets. Large sections shall have stiffening ribs cast on the back, not over 2 feet apart. All miters in cast work shall be cut and filed smooth and the fit made perfect.

All members of drawn or extruded metal shall be framed together at contact points with similar metal, or with cast metal with pins and rivets, or by brazing and welding the metals together. Any solder used in connection with this work shall match the metal in color.

All faces of metal in contact shall be milled to a hair joint with metal to metal, and all joints shall be machined and filed to a close fit. Exposed joints must be lapped flush. All mouldings and ornaments shall be in perfect alignment at joints. Bolt and screw holes must be drilled (not cored), and where exposed they shall be counter-sunk flush. All work shall have the necessary rivets, brackets, fillets, or other reinforcement, all of which shall be of bronze, and the various sections assembled with concealed fasteners.

Where two or more pieces of metal are used in building up members, the contact surfaces shall be brought to a true, smooth and even surface and secured together so that the joints shall be absolutely tight and invisible without the use of pointing. The use of putty or other pointing materials will not be permitted. Where exposed rivets, screws, or bolts can not be avoided they shall be of the same kind of bronze as the parts joined, malleted to the metal and finished to match the color and texture of the adjoining work.

Where exterior doors and elevator doors are constructed with cast and built-up exterior faces and bronze plate sections on the interior face, the interior sections shall be fastened in place with special-head screws as indicated on details.

All doors shall have proper bronze reinforcement for hardware; the stiles and rails shall have fillers of asbestos or cork to deaden metallic sound, and the panels shall be asbestos filled. Sliding doors shall be guaranteed to move easily and readily.

Where hardware is required, the metal shall be properly reinforced and constructed to receive same.

Where hardware is secured with tap screws the metal shall be at least ¼ inch thick to provide a firm hold for the screws and develop the required strength. All work shall be made with proper bevels and clearances on doors and sash so that they will open without binding.

All bronze shall be of the best quality. All castings shall be made from bronze mixture proportioned to produce metal of as near a match in color as possible to the drawn or extruded bronze sections used in connection with the cast work.

[All cast iron shall be new, tough, grey iron, free from blowholes, honeycombs or other defects which would impair its strength or appearance.]

Finish.—All plain surfaces, both flat and moulded, of all bronze work shall be thoroughly cleaned and finished smooth. All ornaments must be delicately hand-chased and finished smooth, with undercutting where necessary so as to restore or faithfully reproduce the details of the models. Filling will be permitted only in connection with ornamental parts and then only the necessary filling consistent with the highest grade of work. The metal used for filling shall be the same as that from which the casting is made and shall match the same in every respect, so that the filling will not be perceptible in the finished work.

All bronze work shall be light golden bronze, oxidized to finish approved by the architects and finished with wax.

[All surfaces of iron work shall be thoroughly cleaned and finished smooth.]

Samples.—Samples of the sections of the ornamented and constructional parts of such units as are required, showing construction and finish, shall be submitted to the architects and receive their approval before the final work is started, and the finished product shall correspond in every detail with that of the approved samples.

Setting.—The contractor for this work is to furnish all hoists, derricks, scaffolds, and other means required for the proper handling and setting of his work in position at the building, leaving his work complete in every respect and satisfactory to the architects.

Cleaning.—On completion all bronze work shall be carefully cleaned down, refinished where necessary and left in perfect condition. All glass shall be washed and cleaned and turned over in a whole and finished manner.

Iron Work.—Contractor for bronze work shall furnish all reinforcements, anchors, iron bucks, track supports, tracks, etc., required for the installation and completion of his work, with the exception of the steel bucks, tracks and hangers and overhead work for main floor elevator doors, which will be furnished and installed under a separate contract.

Surfaces of all iron work shall be thoroughly cleaned and given shop coat of pure red lead and linseed oil. Where required an additional coat of pure red lead and oil shall be applied before erection.

Hardware.—Contractor for bronze work shall furnish all hardware complete as required for the bronze work included in this contract. All finish hardware shall be cast bronze. Standard hardware shall be of the same manufacture as selected for the remainder of the building. Special hardware shall be of manufacture acceptable to the architects. Knobs, handles, push bars, pulls, escutcheons, etc., shall be made from special designs furnished by the architects. All locks shall be cylinder locks, master-keyed and submaster-keyed, as directed.

Glass and Glazing.—The glass for check desks and all glass in connection with the counter-screen and window-screens shall be furnished and installed under this contract.

The tops of check desks shall be constructed of polished plate glass, ¾ inch thick, set on felt of color approved by the architects, at all supporting points of contact.

The glass in connection with counter-screen shall be ¼-inch polished plate glass free from all defects. Glass in counter-screen shall have double-line acid-etched borders. Holes shall be cut in glass for wicket openings and elsewhere as indicated on details, the edges of the openings without bronze frames to be rubbed and polished smooth. All glass for screens of windows of main floor shall be ¼-inch polished plate glass free from all defects. All glass for exterior and interior bronze doors will be furnished and installed under a separate contract.

BRASS

Specifications for brass would be exactly the same as for bronze in respect to everything except finish. In the majority of cases when brass is used in modern architecture it is surface-plated with some non-corrosive metal, such as perhaps silver or gold. Since there are numberless finishes it is impossible here to attempt to enumerate them. When the type of finish has been selected, specification advice can be obtained from the Copper and Brass Research Association, 25 Broadway, New York City (see reference, page 97).

CAST IRON

(Refer to page 116, chapter on Cast Iron, relative to "Estimate Drawings.")

In the matter of specifying cast iron the architect can follow the precedent of bronze in many respects; in fact, it has been suggested that the York & Sawyer bronze specification be used with certain omissions, as to the composition of the metal, of course, and the deletion of all reference to extruded work, finish, chasing, brazing, etc. (page 193). A form follows which embodies the suggestions from several cast iron foundries, as a skeleton to which may be attached the specific conditions of the job in hand.

(See pages 191–192 for "Notice to Bidders," "Workmanship," "Samples," and "Scope.")

Workmanship.—All castings shall be straight, true, sharp, and free from sand holes, cold shuts, pits, and any and all other imperfections. All parts shall be properly jointed and fitted, metal to metal without filling. No joints, screws or other fastening units shall be visible. As far as possible all connections shall be made from the back or inside face of the work. Where it is impossible to avoid having screw heads on the front face, then special screws with projecting lugs shall be used, the lugs to be filed off smooth with the surface of the casting. (If there be a possibility that the parts would ever have to be taken apart, the following sentence may be substituted for the latter: "Where it is impossible to avoid having screw heads on the front face, then the holes for these shall be sufficiently countersunk so that they may be puttied flush with the surface of the casting before painting.") All screws shall be so located as not to interfere with the ornamentation. All warped or crooked castings will be rejected.

Models.—The architect, the modeler and the cast iron contractor shall meet shortly after the awarding of the cast iron contract and decide upon the best way for the models to be made so as to achieve the sharpest and finest results in the castings. The cast iron contractor shall *not* include in his estimate the cost of remaking any models; if however, it is necessary for him to duplicate unit-models for the expedition of his work, such models shall be at his own expense.

It is understood that the modeler shall furnish all full-size models for all ornamentation marked on sheets . . ., as well as both left and right halves of ornamentation wherever necessary. All models of continuous ornament shall be made sufficiently long by the modeler so that the cast iron contractor may be able to make core-boxes or wax duplicates; all returns and intersections shall be properly made; where models are of varying length to fit different dimensions, the necessary supplementary parts shall be carefully made and properly marked. Any damaged models received by the cast iron contractor from the modeler shall be repaired at the expense of the latter. It will be the duty of the cast iron contractor to determine whether all models have been made to the correct shrinkage scale and whether they are in accordance with the dimensions as shown on the architect's approved shop-drawings; in case of any errors he shall notify the modeler which models must be remade, and send a copy of this letter to the architect. The cast iron contractor shall be held responsible for all castings being accurate in all dimensions.

In case there is a discrepancy in dimensions the checked shop-drawings shall take precedence over all others, and all models shall be made in accordance with them. The architect will make changes in models only as they affect ornament and will hold the cast iron contractor responsible that they are in accordance with the checked shop-drawings in every dimension. Any change in the models which the architect may make, affecting the dimensions given in the shop-drawings, shall be noted in a letter by him to the cast iron contractor, but unless changes are authorized in this manner, none will be permitted.

Ornamental castings shall be made *only* from models approved by the architect. When the models are received from the modeler, the cast iron contractor shall notify the architect of their arrival by letter and enumerate them so as to make certain that no unapproved models have been sent.

Samples.—(The same paragraph typical for the various other metals given on page 192 may be inserted, although special stress should be laid on the fact that models should "clearly indicate the ability of the foundry to execute plain surfaces, mouldings, and ornamental modeling, and should be supplemented by photographs showing long pilasters and large panels made in one casting.")

Notifying Architect.—The architect shall be notified when all castings are completed, so that he or his representative may inspect them; work on all rejected items shall be begun immediately so as not to delay the completion of the entire job.

Finishing.—All castings when removed from the sand moulds shall have all foreign clinging matter removed, and all rough surfaces where there have been gates, risers, sprues, etc., ground and filed flush with the surface. The gating and venting shall have been done in such a manner as in no way to interfere with the ornament.

Painting.—[At the foundry—part of cast iron specifications.] All cast iron shall be thoroughly cleaned by sand blasting or by some grease solvent before being painted by the cast iron contractor at the foundry. All surfaces shall then be given one base coat of paint consisting of American vermilion, red lead, or other pigment inhibiting rust, mixed with linseed oil; this shall be painstakingly applied as an *even* coat without any dried ridges of paint showing on the front faces. Only a small percentage of carbon or lamp black will be permitted in this initial coat of paint.

(NOTE.—Instead of painting it is suggested that one of the patented processes as described on page 188 be specified, because this treatment eliminates the

necessity of applying a heavy base coat as a rust inhibitor. The finish is a black matte surface which is superior to black paint in appearance. If a different color be desired, a thin finish coat of paint can readily be overlaid, or certain parts of the design picked out in color. "Parkerizing" is one of the means which may be used.)

Painting.—[At the building—part of painting specifications.] All cast iron shall be thoroughly cleansed of all grease before being painted. All spots which have been scratched bare shall be given a base coat of paint consisting of American vermilion, red lead, or other pigment inhibiting rust, mixed with linseed oil. After this has dried a finishing coat shall be given all cast iron work, under the direction of the architect, of such colors and in such manner as he shall direct. Care shall be exercised to the greatest possible degree so that no unevenness shall result when the paint has dried, nor shall any of the ornament be needlessly obscured by an excessive thickness of paint.

If the architect discovers any superfluous paint which has run down and dried in ridges, he shall have full power to reject the work and require all the paint of that part to be burned off. When the surface has been properly cleaned a new base coat as previously specified shall be given the iron. This shall be done at the painting contractor's expense.

[For any existing cast iron work which is to be painted.] All cast iron work in the existing . . . (location of iron described) shall have all old paint removed by burning or dissolving, and the iron shall then be thoroughly rubbed down until the surface is absolutely smooth and cleansed of all foreign substances which may adhere. All exposed surfaces shall then be given one base coat of paint composed of linseed oil and American vermilion, red lead, or other pigment inhibiting rust; this coat shall be applied evenly. [Finishing coat same as above.]

Delays.—On awarding the contract or shortly thereafter the architect will consult with the cast iron contractor and fix a date when his castings shall be completed. (Similar to time necessary for bronze, page 29.) It shall be the duty of the cast iron contractor to draw up a schedule which will make possible the completion of the work by this date set at the conference. If for any reason whatsoever, on the part of any person or persons concerned, or any influence or condition, the cast iron contractor is prevented from keeping to his schedule, it shall be his duty to so inform Mr. —— of the architect's organization. The cast iron contractor shall be held responsible for his work being completed on the date set, so that if, for reasons beyond his control, he is delayed in the execution of his duties, he shall be able to inform the architect as conditions arise and absolve himself of blame if the final completion be delayed. Even if the architect's organization or the owner are retarding the work, Mr. —— of the architect's organization shall be notified nevertheless.

COPPER

The specifications for ornamental copper should clearly state the manner of forming the various parts of the work, and unless the architect has previously had knowledge of the manner in which this is best accomplished, he should consult with a reliable and artistic craftsman before beginning either drawings or specifications. In the chapter on "Copper" (pages 141–142) there is a brief summary of the various types of work suited to either stamping or *repoussé* methods, but since conditions for any building operation are extremely variable, a mere perusal is not adequate substitution for a visit to a craftsman's shop and an amiable consultation.

The following paragraphs are suggestions for what might be considered as a foundation for the "general conditions" of the ornamental copper specifications preceding the specific conditions.

(See pages 191–192 for "Notice to Bidders," "Workmanship," "Samples," and "Scope.")

Materials.—All copper used in the execution of all ornamental work shall be of the best grade obtainable, and of the thickness as shown and marked on the plans and details for each item. All reinforcing members for all copper work of any nature whatsoever, and any other accessories, such as nails, screws, bolts, rivets, etc., shall be of *copper, bronze or brass only.* If any iron or steel is found to be used, the architect reserves the right to reject all of the work in its entirety and award the contract to another contractor. Any contractor found employing any iron or steel is hereby notified that all of his work shall not only be rejected, but there will be no payment made for any labor, material or any item supplied by him.

[The approved thickness of good construction is discussed under "Design Limitations and Shop Practice" (pages 143–144), and, in the case of stamping, the recommendations there enumerated for thickness of copper should be included at this point.]

Stamping.—The dies for all stamping shall be facsimiles of the approved models furnished by the modeler, and if on inspection by the architect or his representative they shall be adjudged inferior to the highest class of craftsmanship, they shall be made over at the copper contractor's expense and not used until approved by the architect. All stamping shall be done from such thickness of copper that the completed product will be no less than is stated on the plans and details enumerated above under "Scope." All stamping shall result in artistic products which are clean, sharp, true, and exact reproductions of the models; it shall be done with proper and frequent annealing so that no cracks shall occur. All work near the eye level shall have joints made as exact fitting butt joints, welded on the back with copper, and done in such a craftsmanlike manner as to render the joint unnoticeable a few feet away. All joints above the eye level shall be soldered from the *back* only, and all excess solder which appears on the front face shall be carefully removed and the whole left in a workmanlike condition with the joint showing no wider than a fine pencil line. Any work of any character which is not satisfactory to the architect, regardless of where it may be, shall be rejected and replaced as soon as possible after its rejection by the copper contractor at his expense. All undercut parts shall be assembled in such manner as to exactly reproduce the models, with all joints welded or soldered in the approved manner as specified above.

Repoussé.—All *repoussé* work shall be fashioned from sufficiently heavy material so that when the work is completed it shall be at least of the thickness marked on the plans and details enumerated under "Scope." It shall follow the spirit and character of the architect's sketch (or model, as the case may be) in all respects, and shall be approved by the architect before being taken from the pitch block or other material on which it is being made; any and all changes shall be made as directed by the architect before the work leaves the shop. All details and ornament of any nature shall be clean, sharp and without cracks or other flaws. In being worked it shall be properly annealed. Any joints which may be necessary and approved by the architect shall be such as not to interfere with the character of the ornament, and shall be done as specified under "Stamping."

LEAD

The specifications for ornamental lead, like those for other metals, should clearly state the manner of forming the various parts of the work, and unless the architect has previously had knowledge of the manner in which this is best accomplished, he should consult with a reliable and artistic craftsman before beginning either drawings or specifications. In the chapter on "Lead" (pages 156–158) there is a brief summary of the various types of work suited to either cast or *repoussé* methods, but since conditions for any building operation are extremely variable, a mere perusal is not adequate substitution for a visit to a craftsman's shop and an amiable consultation as to the best shop practice.

(See pages 191–192 for "Notice to Bidders," "Workmanship," "Samples," and "Scope.")

Materials.—The lead used in the execution of all ornamental work shall be of the best grade obtainable of virgin lead, containing less than .005 antimony, and weighing not less than 8 pounds to the square foot (in other words, not less than ⅛ inch in thickness). All joints shall be "burned" by the use of a blow-torch, and shall *not* be soldered. All ornament of any nature shall be formed as a part of the background, by being either cast as a part of it simultaneously, or beaten out of the same sheet of lead in *repoussé* work; in no case will any ornamental features be accepted which are applied by sweating, soldering, burning, or attaching by means of pins or dowels. Any work not conforming to these requirements will be rejected at once, and the contractor responsible for same shall at his own expense replace all the discarded work as soon as possible.

Casting.—All castings of ornamental lead work shall be in accordance with the most approved methods in the best practice, and composed of lead such as is specified under "Materials" of these specifications. For interior cast lead work the detail shall be sharp and clean, but for exterior work, as . . . [list of items as leader heads, running bands of ornament, . . . etc.], it shall take on the rough, uneven texture of coarse sand. All lead shall be worked by hand and shall have the character of old English lead work, similar to sample on view in the architect's office. All ornament shall follow exactly the models approved by the architect and sent by the modeler.

Repoussé.—All *repoussé* work shall be fashioned from sufficiently heavy sheets of virgin lead, having less than .005 antimony, and of quality defined under "Materials" of these specifications, so that on completion no part shall be less than ⅛ inch in thickness. All the work shall follow the spirit and character of the architect's sketch (or model, as the case may be) in all respects; all changes ordered by the architect shall be fully carried out, and his approval obtained before the work is sent from the shop. Any changes the contractor has to suggest shall be discussed with the architect before being carried out, and unless permission in writing is obtained from the architect's office, the contractor shall be held responsible for the execution of all work as shown on plans, drawings, and models.

Tinning.—Where tin is to be applied to the surface of lead for ornamentation, it shall be done as follows: the surface shall be scraped and roughened to a depth of about 1/16 of an inch, the area to be tinned shall then be sprinkled with rosin dust, a small blow-torch shall then so melt the tin (in wire form) that it will remain exactly within the bounds of the area designed to be tinned.

ENAMELLING

(Refer to pages 179–180, chapter on "Enamelling.")

Definition.—It is understood that the term "enamelling," as used in this specification, shall mean only *incised vitreous enamel*, which shall be fused with the bronze or silver so as to become an integral part of the metal. In no sense will the term permit the use of any form of liquid enamel which is painted or sprayed, previous to being baked.

Samples.—The contractor submitting an estimate shall accompany it by a sample, which must come up to the standard established by the architect before the estimate will be considered. In the case of tablets or signs, the sample shall include, (1) specimens of the powdered glass which will be fused into the incisions in the metal, (2) at least two letters incised in the metal in readiness for the enamel, and (3) at least two letters filled and finished. This sample of the successful bidder shall be retained by the architect and compared with the materials used in the finished work, and with the quality of the finished product; any and all work which shall not be at least of quality equal to that of the submitted samples shall be rejected.

After the contract is awarded, the successful bidder shall submit full-size details and samples showing the bronze, the enamelled colors, and the finish, all of which shall be selected by the architect for all classes of enamelling, as interior and exterior decoration, name plates, tablets, signs, wickets, panels, etc. [complete list of items having enamel work, and sheet numbers on which they occur in plans and details].

Bronze.—[Or silver.] All bronze shall be at least ⅛ inch in thickness. [Follow by list of items in which it shall be heavier.]

Separate or Applied Letters and Designs.—The metal of all separate or applied letters and designs shall be bronze or silver, and submitted to the architect for his approval. They shall be fitted with the necessary and non-corrosive lugs with which it is intended to fasten said letters or designs to . . . [state material, such as plaster, stone, marble, or whatever it is to be].

Exterior Enamel.—All exterior enamel work shall be guaranteed by the enamel contractor to withstand the elements and changes in temperature for the life of the job, providing of course, that it remains in its original position, and suffers no abuse for which this contractor is not responsible. During this time it is understood that if the enamel should peel, chip, crack, or in any way depart from its perfection when first erected, the enamel contractor shall be in duty bound to replace at his expense any and all unsatisfactory portions with new work of quality satisfactory to the architect.

BIBLIOGRAPHY

✦✦✦✦✦ HILE there are usually a great num-
✦ W ✦ ber of index cards in any good li-
✦✦✦✦✦ brary's catalogue-room on the metals
covered in this book, only a small proportion of them represent documents dealing
with the application of the metals to architecture. Unfortunately the majority of references
generally cover short magazine articles, books
with illustrations of the metals in purely sculptural forms, or catalogues of collections. While
the following list does not pretend to be inclusive
of every volume which treats of the decorative
metals in their relation to architecture, at least it
includes sources which will give a comprehensive
view of the subject. For want of space the
historical notes contained in this book could
only touch upon a very limited portion of the
field, while a perusal of the books listed below
under the heading, "Of importance for historical information," will afford an infinitely
better conception of the subject if the reader
has the time.

BRONZE

Of importance for historical information:
Fortnum, C. Drury E., *Bronzes*. Victoria and Albert
Museum Art Handbooks.
Perry, J. Travenor, *Dinanderie. A History and Descrip-
tion of Mediæval Art Work in Copper, Brass, and
Bronze*. London: G. Allen & Sons, 1910.
Wyatt, Matthew Digby, *Metal Work and Its Artistic
Design*. London: Day & Son, 1852. (Excellent con-
cise descriptions of various processes, followed by
brief historical résumés.)

Of importance for illustrations:
*Le Bronze, le Cuivre, l'Etain, le Plomb: Album I, du
moyen âge au milieu du XVIIIe siècle; Album 2, du
milieu du XVIIIe siècle au milieu du XIXe siècle*.
By Louis Metman and J. L. Vaudoyer. Paris: D. A.
Longuet, 1910.
Décor du Métal; le Cuivre et le Bronze. By Lucien Magne.
Paris: H. Laurens, 1917.
Le Musée des Arts Décoratifs, Palais du Louvre. (Refer-
ence for furniture applications, small panels, etc.)
*Les Nouvelles Collections de l'Union Centrale des Arts
Décoratifs au Musée du Louvre*. Paris: G. Armand
Guérinet, 190-. (Series illustrates periods following
Louis XIV; Nos. 1 and 6 deal mostly with bronze,
No. 11 mostly bronze with some copper and wrought
iron, and No. 15 mostly bronze but also includes
some copper.)
Le Style Empire, 1re, 2e, 3e, et 4e *Séries*. Paris: F. Contet.

BRASS

Chiefly of importance for historical information:
Boutell, C., *Monumental Brasses and Slabs; an His-
torical and Descriptive Notice of the Incised Monu-
mental Memorials of the Middle Ages*. London: Cogs-
well, 1847.
Boutell, C., *The Monumental Brasses of England*. En-
gravings by R. B. Utting. London: Nelson, 1849.
Fortnum, C. Drury E., *Bronzes*. Victoria and Albert
Museum Art Handbooks.
Macklin, Herbert W., *Monumental Brasses*. London:
S. Sonnenshein & Co., 1891.

CAST IRON

There are no historical or illustrative books on this subject isolated by itself, although occasional references
occur in "Ironwork," I, II, and III, by J. Starkie Gardner (Victoria and Albert Museum Art Handbooks). A
collection of photographs of the Heckla Iron Works
is referred to in the text (page 103).

COPPER

Chiefly of interest for historical information:
Burgess, Fred W., *Chats on Old Copper and Brass*. New
York: F. A. Stokes Co., 1914.
Fortnum, C. Drury E., *Bronzes*. Victoria and Albert
Museum Art Handbooks (page 132 for notes on
Limoges school).
Perry, J. Travenor, *Dinanderie. A History and De-
scription of Mediæval Art Work in Copper, Brass, and
Bronze*. London: G. Allen & Sons, 1910.

Chiefly of interest for illustrations of French work (text in
French):
Magne, Lucien, *Décor du Métal, le Cuivre et le Bronze*.
Paris: H. Laurens, 1917.

LEAD

Of foremost importance:
(1) Weaver, Lawrence, *English Leadwork, Its Art and
History*. London: B. T. Batsford, 1909. (Gives a complete historical survey of Continental lead work as
well as English, and among numerous illustrations
gives various examples of interesting seam-designs
on roofs and spires.)
(2) Lethaby, W. R., *Leadwork Old and Ornamental, and
for the Most Part English*. London: Macmillan & Co.,
1893.

Of interest historically:
White, Elizabeth, "Lead and Tin in Art," *International Studio*, 1925.

Of importance for French lead work:
Magne, Lucien, *Décor du Métal; le Cuivre et le Bronze*.
Paris: H. Laurens, 1917.
Metman, Louis, and Vaudoyer, J. L., *Le Bronze, le
Cuivre, l'Etain, le Plomb*, Albums 1 et 2. Paris: D. A.
Longuet, 1910.

Of general interest on the methods of refining lead and
subsequent means of working it for sundry uses:
Harn, O. C., *Lead, the Precious Metal*. New York:
The Century Co., 1924.

INDEX OF ILLUSTRATIONS

(Author's Note: The "List of Illustrations," which is usually included in the front matter of a book, has been omitted because there seemed to be no useful purpose served by a series of 277 titles. It seemed sufficient to have only the following index, which classifies the illustrations according to subject-matter; when the book is being used as a design reference guide illustra-tions can be found under subject headings, *e. g.*, "Balconies, cast iron," not "Cast iron bal-conies." The illustrations of various metals are grouped in separate chapters which are obvi-ously designated on the Contents page, and since they are thus easily referred to, the titles of all illustrations of any one metal are not re-peated here.)

NOTE: ALL NUMERALS REFER TO *Figure* NUMBERS.